Gardening Indoors

Revised Edition for the 1990's

Gardening Indoors

by George F. Van Patten

I would like to express my sincere thanks to all of the wonderful gardeners that help to make this book a reality. Many individuals and stores contributed information, photos an drawings. Thank you all for your help in making *Gardening Indoors, The Revised Edition for the 1990's* the best possible book.

A special thanks to *Growing Edge Magazine* for suppling us with numerous drawings and photographs.

Published and distributed by Van Patten Publishing, Portland, Oregon.

Artwork: D. B. Turner, Connie Cohen, *Growing Edge Magazine*
Book Design: G. F. Van Patten
Cover Photo: Courtesy American Hydroponics, Arcata, California
Back Cover Photo of British Columbian gardener: Tom Alexander, *Growing Edge Magazine*

Editors: Jim Estes, Roger Thayer

Table of Contents

Introduction

This *Revised Edition for the 1990's* is updated by a new author, George F. Van Patten. George has rewritten sections on lighting, hydroponics and nutrients. These new sections reflect state-of-the-art changes in indoor gardening. George has also removed most references to chemical disease and insect control to reflect the major shift to natural, organic controls.

This book provides a simple, complete, how to description of basic gardening techniques used to grow foliage and pot plants, flowers and vegetables indoors today. Horticulture is the art and science of growing plants. High Intensity Discharge (HID) lamps have made indoor gardening grow by leaps and bounds. Today it is possible to grow large quantities of fresh tomatoes, cucumbers, succulents and all kinds of flowers in your own home all year round.

Many factors should be considered when gardening indoors. To have the best garden possible, you will need to monitor and control all environmental factors and understand the needs of your plants. Which environmental factors have indoor horticulturists found to be most important for a productive and healthy garden? What are the most common obstacles faced by indoor gardeners?

 RULES OF THUMB are given for a quick, easy reference. They are an easy-to-remember guide that is somewhere between an educated guess and a scientific formula. The **RULES OF THUMB** give everyone a feel for the task or subject.

This book deals mainly with annual flowers and vegetables. We refer to these plants as annuals throughout the text. If the plants you are growing do not fit in this category, look up the specific growing conditions (temperature, humidity, light etc.) requirements in the "Plant Selection Guide" in Chapter Eleven.

Publications such as *Growing Edge, Organic Gardening, 21st Century Gardener, National Gardening, Horticulture, Fine Gardening, Flower & Garden, Sunset,* and *Harrowsmith Magazines* and the gardening section of the local newspaper offer valuable background information on gardening. Reading such publications regularly will keep you updated on the newest trends in gardening.

SECTION I
The Indoor Environment

Chapter One

Indoor Gardening

The key to successful gardening is to understand how a plant produces food and grows. Plants may be cultivated indoors or out, but still have the same requirements for growth. All plants needs light, air, water, nutrients, a growing medium, and heat to manufacture food and to grow. Without any one of these essentials, growth will stop and death result. Of course, the light must be of the proper spectrum and intensity; air must be warm, arid, and rich in carbon dioxide; water must be abundant, and the growing medium must be warm and contain the proper levels of nutrients. When all these needs are met consistently, at levels, optimum growth results.

Most flowers and vegetables are normally grown as annual plants, completing their life cycle in one year. A seed or bulb that is planted in the spring will grow strong and tall through the summer and flower in the fall, producing more seeds. The annual cycle starts all over again, with the new seeds. Marigolds, zinnias, tomatoes and lettuce are just a few examples of annual plants.

Biennials are plants that normally complete their life cycle in two years. They bloom the year after seeds are planted, and die after flowering and producing seed the second year. Examples of biennials are pansies, hollyhocks, foxglove, parsley, Brussels sprouts and beets.

Perennial plants live for two years or more. Leafy perennials are valued for their lush and interesting foliage. These plants may also bloom the flowers are secondary to their foliage.

Plants in this category include the Benjamin fig, photographs and elephant ear philodendrons.

Flowering perennials generally have shorter blooming seasons and may or may not remain green all year round. Examples of this group are wisteria, clematis, azaleas and vinca.

The seed has an outside coating, to protect the embryo plant, and a supply of stored food within. Given favorable conditions, including moisture, heat and air, a healthy seed will usually germinate. The seed's coating splits, a rootlet grows downward, and a sprout with seed leaves pushes upward in search of light. A seedling is born!

The single root from the seed grows down and branches out, similar to the way the stem branches out above ground. Tiny rootlets draw in water and nutrients (chemical substances needed for life). Roots also serve to anchor a plant in the ground. As the plant matures, the roots take on specialized functions. The center and old, mature portions contain a water transport system and may also store food. The tips of the roots produce elongating cells that continue to push farther and farther into the soil in quest of more water and food. The single celled root hairs are the parts of the root that actually absorb water and nutrients, but must be in the presence of oxygen. Without water and air these frail root hairs will dry up and die. They are very delicate and may easily be damaged by light, air or careless hands if moved or exposed. Extreme care must be exercised during transplanting to ensure success.

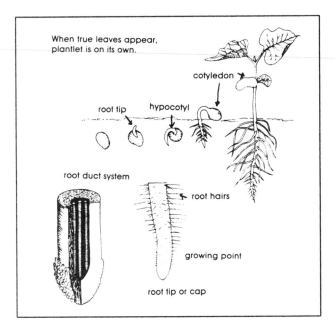

When true leaves appear, plantlet is on its own.

cotyledon

root tip   hypocotyl

root duct system

root hairs

growing point

root tip or cap

for photosynthesis to occur, the leaf's interior tissue must be kept moist. The stomata open and close to regulate the flow of moisture, preventing dehydration. Plant leaves are also protected from drying out by an outer skin. The stomata also permit the outflow of water vapor and waste oxygen. The stomata are very important to the plant's well-being and must be kept clean at all times to promote vigorous growth. Dirty, clogged stomata breathe about as well as you would with a sack over your head!

Stomata on leaf underside

Like the roots, the stem grows through elongation, also producing new buds along the stem. The central or terminal bud carries growth upward; side or lateral buds turn into branches or leaves. The stem functions by transmitting water and nutrients from the delicate root hairs to the growing buds leaves, and flowers. Sugars and starches, manufactured in the leaves, are distributed through the plant via the stem. This fluid flow takes place near the surface of the stem. If the stem is bound too tightly by string or other tie-downs, it will cut the flow of life-giving fluids, thereby strangling and killing the plant. The stem also supports the plant with stiff cellulose, located in the inner walls. Outdoors, rain and wind push a plant around, causing production of much stiff cellulose to keep the plant supported upright. Indoors, with no natural wind or rain present, stiff cellulose is minimal and plants may need to be staked up, especially during flowering.

Once the leaves expand, they start to manufacture food (carbohydrates). Chlorophyll, the substance that gives plants their green color, converts carbon dioxide (CO_2) from the air, water (containing nutrients) and light energy into carbohydrates and oxygen. This process is called photosynthesis. It requires water drawn up from the roots, through the stem, into the leaves where it encounters CO_2. Tiny pores located on the underside of the leaf, called stomata (Stomata can be spelled several ways - stomatae, stoma or stomata - in this book we will spell it stomata) funnel CO_2 into contact with the water. In order

Most flowers and vegetables will flower if conditions are right; for short-day plants, the main variable is the photoperiod. In the fall, the days become shorter and plants are signaled that the annual life cycle is coming to an end. The plant's functions change. Leafy growth slows and flowers start to form. The majority of long-day plants bloom according to chronological age. That is, when they are two or three months old, they start to bloom. Flowers such as marigolds, petunias, pansies, cosmos, California poppies, zinnias etc. will continue to bloom once flowering starts. Long-day vegetables will set blossoms that soon drop when fruit forms in the wake of the lower. Many common vegetables such as tomatoes, peppers, egg plants, squash etc. fall into this category. Vegetables grown for their roots (carrots, potatoes, onions) generally bloom before the final underground produce is ripe. Leaf crops such as lettuce, spinach, parsley etc. are very productive indoors. All parts of these crops are consumed and little concern about maturity is needed.

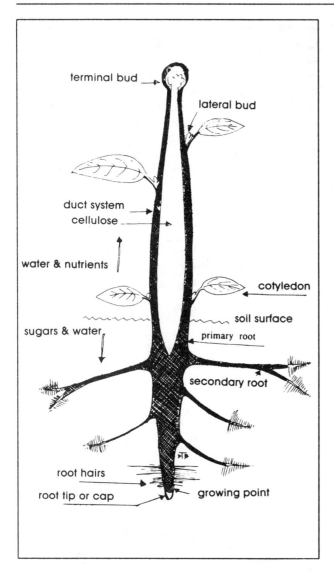

Some plants have both male and female flowers. When both female and male flowers are in bloom, pollen from the male flower lands on the female flower, thereby fertilizing it. The male dies after producing and shedding as much pollen as possible. Seeds form and grow within the female flowers. As the seeds are maturing, the female plant slowly dies. The mature seeds then fall to the ground and germinate naturally or are collected for planting the next spring.

Indoor vs. Outdoor Gardening

Gardening indoors is very different from outdoor cultivation, even though all plants have standard requirements for growth. The critical factors of the outdoor environment must be totally recreated indoors if a plant is to grow well. Outdoors, a gardener can expend a minimum of effort and Mother Nature will control many of the growth-influencing factors. Indoors, the horticulturist assumes the cherished role of Mother Nature. The horticulturist is able to wield control over many factors influencing growth. Since few people have ever played Mother Nature before, they usually do not fathom the scope of the job. We must realize that Mother Nature constantly provides the many things plants require to grow. The indoor gardener must manufacture the most important elements of the outdoor environment. This requires a general knowledge of the environment about to be created, as well as specific guidelines to follow.

Outdoor cultivation is normally limited to one growing season. However, two or more growing seasons are possible in semitropic and tropical climates. Outdoors, light can be inadequate, especially if it is midwinter and you live in a city or an apartment or both. Outdoor air is usually fresh, but can become uncontrollably humid, arid, cold or windy. Water and nutrients are usually easy to supply, but acid salts could keep the nutrients unavailable to the plants.

With indoor horticulture, light, air, temperature, humidity, ventilation, CO_2, soil, water and nutrients may be precisely controlled to yield a perfect environment for plant growth.

Not long ago, with fluorescent tubes, this was not true. An inexpensive, easy-to-manage artificial light source, providing adequate intensity, was the main factor that limited growing many varieties of plants indoors.

Technological breakthroughs and scientific research have shed bright light on indoor horticulture, by producing the metal halide and High Pressure (HP) sodium, High Intensity Discharge (HID) lamps. Now a reasonably priced artificial light source, providing the color spectrum and intensity necessary to grow any plant imaginable, is on the market. With the HID lamp, a gardener can totally control the indoor environment. The high pressure sodium lamp can be used in conjunction with a halide or in a greenhouse to augment the sun. Conversion bulbs that burn a HP sodium arc tube in a metal halide system are also available. The HP sodium emits a light spectrum similar to the autumn or harvest sun, providing the intense yellows, oranges and reds necessary for forming large flowers. When an HP sodium lamp is used, flowers grow 20 to 100 percent larger than if only a single metal halide were used. The HID lamp is essentially a small sun in your basement, spare room or attic. By using a timer, a regular day-night schedule (photoperiod) can be set up. The HID, with a timer, may be even better than the sun! Exact control can be exercised over the hours of light per day. This control of day length lets the horticulturist create his or her own seasons. Spring and summer and fall are recreated over and over, winter is forgotten and virtually non-existent to the indoor horticulturist!

In climates where the season is "long" (eight or nine months) a much larger selection of flowers and vegetables can be cultivated. Gardeners living in northern climates can grow tomatoes in containers outdoors until the weather cools, then move them under the halide in the basement for a complete winter crop.

Healthy cauliflower is just forming under a super metal halide.

Halides are also used very effectively to get an early start on annuals and vegetables. Since HID's are so bright, the little plantlets get a very strong start in life. This strong, early start is carried on throughout life.

Flowers and vegetables can also be grown in a greenhouse. The HP sodium lamp works extremely well to provide supplemental light to natural sunlight. Young seedlings get an early start with more hours of light per day; fruit or flowers that are normally late can be forced to produce faster. All of the extra hours of intense light will make them think it is midsummer!

Outdoors, seeds are normally sown in the spring, mature and bear fruit and flowers in the summer.

Indoors, all growth factors may be individually controlled to give the plant exactly what it needs to promote any stage of growth.

The air outdoors is usually fresh and contains .03 to .04 percent CO_2. Ventilation is usually adequate, but the wind sometimes howls, burning leaves or even blowing plants over. Humidity and temperature are almost impossible to control.

Indoors, air may easily be controlled to promote growth and create an unfriendly environment for bugs and fungus. The CO_2 content may be enriched to double or triple plant growth. An open door and forced-air ventilation system will provide circulation and ventilation necessary to keep air fresh. Humidity is raised by misting the air with water or letting water evaporate from a bucket. Humidity is lowered by drying the air with heat from the HID system, heater, furnace or dehumidifier. Circulation, ventilation, humidity and temperature regulation are also fundamental to insect and fungus control. Cuttings root much faster in a warm, humid indoor environment. Temperature is easy to keep constant. Usually heat from the HID system provides ample heat for the grow room. An indoor garden will flourish between 70 and 75° F (21 and 24° C), but most cuttings root best at 80 to 85° F (27 to 30° C). Air temperature may be raised with extra heat and lowered by means of an exhaust fan attached to a thermostat, if outside air is cooler.

Outdoor soil may vary greatly. It could be too acidic or alkaline, have toxic qualities, drain poorly, be full of harmful insects, fungus and bad micro-organisms.

Indoor growing mediums can be purchased from a nursery in the form of potting soil or soilless mix. These growing mediums are generally certified free of fungus, insects and weeds. These growing mediums normally have the proper acid-to-alkaline or pH balance. Potting soils usually contain complete, balanced nutrients, while soilless mixes may or may not be fortified with nutrients. Nutrient levels may easily be checked in these growing mediums. Nutrients may then be added or leached (washed) out of containers, providing total soil control. The moisture content of the growing medium can be precisely monitored with a moisture meter and controlled. Potting soil and soilless mixes are blended to retain water evenly, provide good aeration, and consistent root growth.

Outdoors, insects and fungi are usually kept in check by Mother Nature. Indoors, the gardener must take over in Mother Nature's absence. Keep the insects out of the grow room by simple sanitary precautions. It is easy to wash your hands, use clean tools and sweep the floor regularly. If insects and fungus do get started, they are easy to control in an enclosed room, since the gardener controls the factors that inhibit their well-being. Organic or chemical sprays are used in conjunction with humidity, ventilation and temperature regulation to control the pests.

In summary, indoor gardening can be far superior to outdoor cultivation for many gardeners, especially in northern climates. It provides exacting control of all growth-inducing factors. The indoor garden yields vine ripened produce, flowers and exotic plants the year round!

About Grow Rooms

The best location for a grow room is an unused corner of the basement. The basement is probably the best room in most homes for indoor gardens, since the temperature is easy to keep constant the year round. Humidity that would destroy the rest of the house can be easily managed in the plant room. Insecticides can be used without endangering the entire family. The unsightly pots, soil and flats do not have to be shared with the public. The room is well insulated by concrete walls and soil. Basements also remain cool, which helps prevent heat build up.

The size of the grow room and the light intensity required by plants grown determine the wattage of lamp used. A 400-watt lamp are just fine for smaller rooms, spaces from 10 to 40 square feet of floor space. A 1000-watt bulb should be employed for a grow room of 50 to 100 square feet.

The drawings on page 13 show several common grow room floor plans. As the drawings of rooms demonstrate, there are several basic approaches to grow room production. The climate you create in the grow room depends on the plants that are grown.

A second method is very similar to the first, but utilizes two rooms. The first room is for vegetative growth, rooting cuttings and growing seedlings. Since plants are small, the room is about a third to half the size of the flowering room. The flowering room is harvested and the vegetative crop is moved into the flowering room. A crop of cuttings is transplanted into large pots to start the vegetative cycle.

A third method provides a perpetual crop. Several clones are taken each day or two. An equal same amount of plants are moved from the vegetative room to the flowering room. Of course the harvest is essentially perpetual!

About Greenhouses

Greenhouses or growing environments using natural and artificial lighting are very productive. The same principles can be applied to both the indoor grow room and the greenhouse. However the heat and light intensity might be substantially different.

When combined with natural sunlight, artificial light is most optimally used during non-daylight hours. Greenhouse growers turn the HID lights on when sunlight diminishes, and off when sunlight strengthens.

Turn the HID on when the daylight intensity is less than two times the intensity of the HID. Measure this point with a light meter.

Turn the HID off when the daylight intensity is greater than two times the intensity of the HID.

 RULE OF THUMB: Turn the HID "on" in the greenhouse at sunset and "off" at sunrise.

Supplementary lighting has greatest effect when applied to the youngest plants. It is least expensive to light plants when they are small. This should be considered when budgets are concerned.

One greenhouse is double-glazed on the south, east and west walls and insulated with a reflective interior on the north side.

Developed in England, this cool-weather structure is called the Northern Light Greenhouse. Available from Gardeners Supply, 128 Intervale Road, Burlington, VT 05401.

Setting Up The Grow Room

Before any plants are introduced, the grow room should be set up. Construction requires space and planning. There are a few things that need to be accomplished before the room is ready for plants.

STEP ONE: Choose an out-of-the-way space with little or no traffic. A dark corner in the basement is perfect. Make sure the room is the right size. A 1000-watt HID, properly set up, will efficiently illuminate *up to* a 10-by-10-foot room if a "light mover" (pages 37-40) is used. The ceiling should be at least 5 feet high. Remember, plants are set up about one foot off the ground in containers and the lamp needs about a foot of space to hang from the ceiling. This leaves only three feet of space for plants to grow. However, if forced to grow in an attic or basement with a low, 4-foot ceiling, much can be done to compensate for the loss of height, including cloning, bending and pruning.

STEP TWO: Enclose the room, if it's not already enclosed. Remove everything not having to do with the garden. Furniture, and especially drapes or curtains harbor many a fine fungus. Having the room totally enclosed will permit easy, precise control of everything and everyone that enters and exits, and who and what goes on inside. For most gardeners, enclosing the grow room is simply a matter of tacking up some sheet rock in the basement or attic and painting it flat white.

A vent fan and an oscillating circulation fan are necessary for adequate ventilation and circulation in a grow room.

STEP THREE: See: "Setting Up the Vent Fan" pages: 99-100. Constant circulation and a supply of *fresh* air are essential. There should be at least one fresh-air vent in a 10-by-10-foot room, preferably two. The fresh air vent may be an open door, window or heat vent. Most gardeners have found that a small exhaust fan, vented outdoors,

pulling new *fresh* air through an open door will create an ideal air flow. A small oscillating fan works well for circulation. When installing such a fan, make sure it is not set in a fixed position, blowing too hard on tender plants. It could cause windburn, or in the case if young seedlings and clones, dry them out. If the room contains a heat vent, it may be opened to supply extra heat or air circulation.

STEP FOUR: The larger your garden gets, the more water it will need. A 10-by-10-foot garden may need as much as 30 gallons a week. You may carry water in, one container at a time. One gallon of water weighs 8 pounds). It is much easier to install a hose with an on/off valve or install a hose bib in the room. A 3 to 4-foot watering wand can be attached to the hose on/off valve. The wand will save many broken branches when watering in dense foliage. Hook the hose up to a hot and cold water source, so the water temperature can be regulated easily.

STEP FIVE: Cover walls, ceiling, floor, everything, with a highly reflective material such as flat white paint (pages 34-37). The more reflection, the more light energy that is available to plants. Good reflective light will allow effective coverage of a 1000-watt HID lamp to increase from 36 square feet, with no reflective material, to a maximum of 100 square feet, just by putting $10 to $20 worth of paint on the walls.

STEP SIX: A concrete floor or a smooth surface that can be swept and washed down is ideal. A floor drain is also very handy. In grow rooms with carpet or wood floors, a large, white, painter's dropcloth or thick white visqueen plastic, will save floors from moisture drainage. A tray can also be placed beneath each container for added protection and convenience.

STEP SEVEN: Mount a hook, strong enough to support 30 pounds, in the center of the growing area to be serviced by the lamp. Attach an adjustable chain or cord and pulley between the ceiling hook and the lamp fixture. The adjustable cord makes it easy to keep the lamp at the proper distance from the growing plants and up out of the way when maintaining them.

CAUTION! A hot HID may break if touched by a few drops of cold water. Be very careful and make sure to move the HID out of the way when servicing the garden.

STEP EIGHT: There are some tools an indoor gardener must have and a few extra tools that make indoor horticulture much more precise and cost-effective. The extra tools help the horticulturist play Mother Nature, and make the garden so efficient that they pay for themselves quickly. Purchase all the tools or hunt them up around the house before the plants are moved into the room. If the tools are available when needed, chances are they will be used. A good example is a hygrometer. If plants show signs of slow, sickly growth due to high humidity, most gardeners will not notice the exact cause right away. They will wait and guess, wait and guess, and maybe figure it out before a fungus attacks, and the plant dies. When a hygrometer is installed *before* the plants are in the grow room, the horticulturist will know, from the start, when the humidity is too high and causing sickly growth. The majority of long-day plants bloom according to chronological age. That is, when they are two or three months old, they start to bloom. Flowers such as marigolds, petunias, pansies, cosmos, California poppies, zinnias etc. will continue to bloom once flowering starts. Long-day vegetables will set blossoms that soon drop when fruit forms in the wake of the lower. Many common vegetables such as tomatoes, peppers, egg plants, squash etc. fall into this category. Vegetables grown for their roots (carrots, potatoes, onions) generally bloom before the final underground produce is ripe. Leaf crops such as lettuce, spinach, parsley etc. are very productive indoors. All parts of these crops are consumed and little concern about maturity is needed.

STEP NINE: Read and complete: "Setting Up the HID Lamp" at the end of Chapter Two.

STEP TEN: Move in the seedlings or rooted clones into the room. Huddle them closely together under the lamp. Make sure the HID is not so close to the small plants that it burns their leaves. Usually seedlings require the lamp to be at least 24 inches away.

PLASTIC DROP CLOTH

Necessary Tools	**Extra Tools**
Thermometer	pH & soil test kit
Spray bottle	Hygrometer
Pruner or scissors	Wire (bread sack) ties
Notebook	Merasuring cup & spoons
Yardstick (to measure growth)	Moisture meter

Chapter Two

Light, Lamps and Electricity

Light is one of the major factors that contribute to plant growth. Indoors, light has been, until recent years, the main limiting factor to growing more than a small indoor garden of limited plant varieties. By understanding how a plant uses light, the indoor horticulturist can use the technology provided by the High Intensity Discharge (HID) lamps to fulfill light requirements and grow spectacular gardens. The subject of light as used by plants can become very complex. This book will look at the basic ways light affects plant growth.

A plant combines light energy with carbon dioxide (CO_2), water and nutrients to form green chlorophyll and carbohydrates, releasing oxygen as a by-product. Without light, a plant will not be able to produce green chlorophyll; leaves soon turn yellow, and eventually death results. With the proper spectrum and intensity of light, chlorophyll is rapidly produced and rapid growth occurs.

Outdoors, the sun usually supplies enough light for rapid growth. The sun also supplies much light that plants do not use. Scientists have found that plants need and use only certain portions of the light spectrum. The most important colors in the spectrum for maximum chlorophyll production and photosynthetic response are in the blue (445 nm) and red (650 nm) range. "nm" = nanometers. One nm = .000001 meter. Light is measured in wavelengths, the wavelengths are divided into nm.

Phototropism is the movement of a plant part (foliage) toward illumination. Positive tropism means the foliage moves toward the light.

Negative tropism means the plant part moves away from the light. Positive tropism is greatest in the blue end of the spectrum at about 450 nm. At this optimum level, plants lean toward the light, spreading their leaves out horizontally to absorb the most light possible.

The photoperiod is the relationship between the length of the light period and dark period. The photoperiod affects the life cycle of all plants. Short-day plants will stay in the vegetative growth stage as long as a photoperiod of 18 to 24 hours light is maintained. Sixteen to 24 hours of light per day will give short day plants all the light they need to sustain optimum seedling and vegetative growth. The plants will think it is the longest and sunniest day (June 22) every day of the year. Many plants can use 16 to 18 hours of light in a 24-hour period before a point of diminishing returns is reached. The light has a minimal effect on growth after 16 to 18 hours.

Greatest efficiency is obtained by adding supplemental light to a greenhouse crop after the sun goes down. The HID lights are not as bright as the sun and should not compete with the sun. Plants can also reach a maximum saturation point; the extra light they receive does not increase growth in relation to the amount of light shed. After this point of diminishing returns is reached, additional light has only a minimal effect. If this supplemental light is added during dark periods or on very cloudy days, plants get the entire benefit of the supplemental lighting. Many experiments have proven that adding supplemental light during the dark hours is 50 to 100 percent more productive than adding more light during sunlight hours.

A plant will only grow as fast as the least available factor will allow.

Flowering is induced most efficiently in short-day plants with 12 to 14 hours of *uninterrupted darkness* in a 24-hour photoperiod. It is possible to gradually decrease the daylight hours while increasing dark hours to simulate the natural photoperiod. This practice follows the natural photoperiod but it flowering is delayed for several weeks.

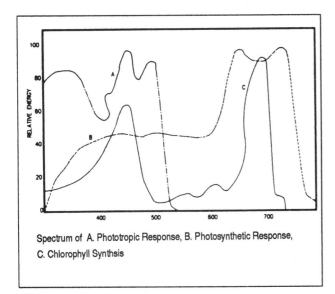

Spectrum of A. Phototropic Response, B. Photosynthetic Response, C. Chlorophyll Synthsis

Light Spectrum Chart

Optimum flowering potential is reached when the 12-hour photoperiod is coupled with high levels of intense light from the red end of the spectrum. After short-day plants are two to 12 months old, altering the photoperiod to an even 12 hours, day and night, will induce flowering in two to four weeks. The 12-hour photoperiod represents the classic equinox and is the optimum daylight-to-dark relationship for flowering. For most of the plants that fall in this category, less than 12 hours of light will not induce flowering any faster and can substantially reduce flower formation and yield.

More than 12 hours of light will prolong flowering; visible signs of flower formation take much longer.

The photoperiod can also be the signal to stay in (or revert to) vegetative growth. Short-day plants must have 12 hours of uninterrupted, total darkness to flower properly. Tests have shown that even dim light during the dark period in the pre-flowering and flowering stages will prevent short-day plants from blooming. Chrysanthemums, for example, are forced to bloom at various times of the year by interrupting their nighttime with a few 10-to-30 minute bursts of bright light.

When the 12-hour dark period is interrupted by light, the plant gets confused by the light's signal saying, "It's daytime, start vegetative growth." The plant will try to revert to vegetative growth and flowering seems to take forever. Make sure to keep flowering short-day plants in total darkness; no midnight visits or lit-up open doorways!

Gardeners growing tropical plants (orchids or bromeliads) from equatorial regions give their gardens 12 hours of light throughout the life cycle. They want to replicate the less dynamic photoperiod of the tropics. On the equator, days and nights are almost exactly the same length the year round. When this method is used, plants tend to bloom when they are chronologically ready, after thoroughly completing the vegetative growth stage.

The average house plant is "night neutral" since it will grow and bloom well with six to eight hours of darkness. These plants require 14 to 16 hours of daylight. Examples of these "night neutral" plants include most gesneraids, oxalis, Exacum affine, many begonias, and most house plants.

Chrysanthemums, poinsettias, species columnea, orchids and some begonias, Christmas cactus and related plants will bloom only if given a long night of 14 to 16 hours and less than eight to 10 hours of light per day.

Summer-blooming plants and vegetables need 18 hours of light per day and a short night of six hours. Geraniums, annuals, tuberous begonias and seedlings of almost all plants are in this category. In fact,   African violets will double their blossom production if they are given 18 hours of light rather than 12 hours.

Foliage plants are raised for green foliage; flowers are not important. These plants can have varying amounts of light and dark and growth is not affected. Examples are rex begonias, aroids, palms, marantas and ferns.

Intensity

HID's are incredibly bright! It is this brightness that makes them so useful. However, this intense light must be properly managed to grow a bumper crop. Intensity is the magnitude of light energy per unit of area. It is greatest near the source of the light and diminishes with distance from the source. The drawing below demonstrates how rapidly light intensity diminishes. Plants that are 4 feet away from the lamp, get a fourth as much light as plants one foot away! The closer plants are to the light source, the better they grow. Six inches to 12 inches is a safe distance for plants to be from the lamp (tender seedlings require 24 inches to 36 inches). Any closer and plants run the risk of growing so fast that they run into the hot bulb, burning tender growing tips.

A 1000-watt standard metal halide emits 100,000 initial lumens and 88,000 mean (average) lumens - *super* halides emit 125,000 initial lumens and 100,000 mean lumens. The HP sodium emits a whopping 140,000 initial lumens! The indoor horticulturist is interested in how much light is *emitted* by the HID, as well as how much light is *received* by the plants. Light that is received is measured by the "Light and Distance Chart", or in watts-per-square-foot or in foot-candles (f.c.). One foot-candle equals the amount of light that falls on one square foot of surface located one foot away from one candle. One lumen is equal to the amount of light emitted by one candle that falls on one square foot of surface one foot away.

Watts-per-square feet is easy to calculate, but not very accurate. It measures how many watts are available from a light source in a given area. For example, a 1000-watt HID will emit an average of 10 watts-per-square foot in a 10-by-10-foot room. The mounting height of the lamp is not considered in watts-per-square foot; the lamp could be mounted at any height, from 4 to 8 feet.

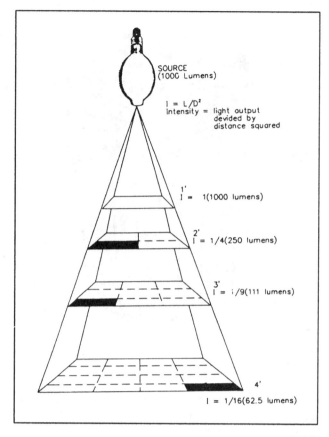

SOURCE
(1000 Lumens)

$I = L/D^2$
Intensity = light output devided by distance squared

1'
$I = 1(1000$ lumens$)$

2'
$I = 1/4(250$ lumens$)$

3'
$I = 1/9(111$ lumens$)$

4'
$I = 1/16(62.5$ lumens$)$

Calculating foot-candles is the most accurate way to estimate the amount of light plants receive. Foot-candles can be measured with a light meter. The meter can measure in footcandles, miliwatts-per-square-meter or lumens. A photographic light meter, either hand-held or built into a camera can also be used. The footcandle meter is simply pointed at the light source or reflective surface at any location, and a read-out in foot-candles is given.

When using a photographic light meter, set the ASA (film speed) at 200 and the shutter speed at 1/125 second. Focus the camera on a rigid white sheet of paper in the proposed plant location. Hold the paper so it gets maximum illumination. Get close enough so all the camera or light meter sees is the white paper. Adjust the camera lens aperture (f stop) until a correct exposure registers on the light meter. Use the following chart to calculate footcandles (f.c.).

f4	64 f.c.
f5.6	125 f.c.
f8	250 f.c.
f11	500 f.c.
f16	1000 f.c.
f22	2000 f.c.

Almost all the resent light research in relation to plants that is available was done by European scientists or scientists and expressed in watts-per-square-meter or miliwatts-per-square-meter. You will need to convert foot-candles to watts-per-square-meter to get the most out of this chapter. Please notice that each lamp and natural sunlight have *different* conversion factors. The conversion factors are found in the chart below.

CONVERSION CHART

Formula:
One: Multiply the footcandle reading by the conversion factor for the light source. Look at the "Conversion Factors Chart" below to obtain the number of watts-per-square-meter.
Two: For mixed lighting (using multiple sources) determine the watts per square meter level for each light source and add the readings for the total.

Examples:
One: A site has 100 footcandles of daylight and 100 footcandles of HP sodium light.
Daylight: 100 X 0.055 = 5.5 watts-per-square-meter
HP sodium light: 100 X 0.034 = 3.4 watts-per-square-meter
Total: 5.5 = 3.4 = 8.9 watts-per-square-meter

This drawing shows the light distribution curve for the PL-780, a Dutch 400 watt horizontal HP sodium lamp.

Two: A grow room has 100 foot-candles of HP sodium light and 100 foot-candles of metal halide light.
HP sodium light: 100 X 0.034 = 3.4 watts per square meter
Metal halide light: 100 X 0.34 = 3.4 watts per square meter
Total: 3.4 = 3.4 = 6.8 watts per square meter

CONVERSION FACTORS CHART

Determies watts-per-square-meter for various light sources

Light Source	Conversion factor
Daylight	0.055
HP sodium lamp	0.034
LP sodium lamp	0.022
Metal halide lamp	0.034
Cool white fluorescent	0.030
Warm white fluorescent	0.30
Fluorescent grow lamps	0.044
Incandescent lamps	0.090

Plants are too close to the lights when they are (sun) bleached, or have curled or stunted leaves. Move plants demonstrating these symptoms farther away from the lamp. Plants that require more light should be set up closer to the lamp. Use a stand or overturned container to set them on.

An inexpensive light meter will help you get the most out of your lamp.

Try this simple test with a light meter. You will see how rapidly light intensity diminishes.

One of the best ways to demonstrate how light intensity can retard a harvest is found in an outdoor vegetable garden. Have you ever planted 65-day broccoli that took 100 days to mature? Think about it. Did the plants get full sun all day long? It is assumed that the seeds were planted at the peak of the season and perfect temperatures prevailed. Plants that got less light matured slowly, and produced less than ones getting full sun all day long.

RULE OF THUMB: Plants with high light requirements but receive less intense or filtered light will yield less and mature later.

Light Requirement Categories for All Plants

Milliwatts per square meter ((mWm^2) is the irradiance produced by one-thousandth of a watt of light energy beamed into a surface of one square meter.

3,000 mWm^2: Lighting after flower induction (forcing) during the latter part of cultivation; growing long-day plants, giving a little growth stimulation as well.

4,500 mWm^2: Cultivation of vegetables, flowers (for produce and flowers) through harvest; young spaced vegetative plants.

6,000 mWm^2: For rooting and young plants while still packed under the HID; high light vegetables, flowers (for produce and flowers) plants.

7,500 mWm^2: Rooting some nursery stock and some high-light plants.

9,000 mWm^2: Expensive plants; fast and programmed crops; special cases. Producing this much supplemental light in a room is very expensive.

The U.S. Department of Agriculture will provide data to help determine the amount of light (radiant energy or flux) various plants need to fulfill their light requirements in different stages of their life.

When combined with natural sunlight, artificial light is optimally used during non-daylight hours. Greenhouse growers turn the HID lights on when the point of diminishing returns is reached. The time to turn on or off the HID is when daylight reaches twice the intensity of the HID.

For Example: Turn the HID on when the daylight intensity is less than twice the intensity of the HID. Measure this point with a light meter. A photo cell can also be used to turn one or several HID's on and off when this point is reached.

Turn the HID off when the daylight intensity is greater than twice the intensity of the HID.

 RULE OF THUMB: Turn HID's in a greenhouse "on" at sunset and "off" at sunrise.

Supplementary lighting has the most dynamic effect when applied to the youngest plants. It is least expensive to light plants when they are small, a very important consideration when budgets are concerned.

Spacing

Ideally plants should be spaced under lamps so that they do not touch one another. This provides for more air movement and allow enough growing space for each plant. Proper spacing also allows more even light saturation.

Bedding plants are given a level of 6,000 mWm^2 for 16 to 18 hours a day. This extra light gives the little plants a big jump on the season outdoors. The intense light also keeps many plants blooming all year long indoors.

When light intensity is too low, plants s-t-r-e-t-c-h for it. Low light intensity is often caused by the lamp being too far away. When the plant is too far away, branches usually form farther apart on the stem than if the lamp were close to plants. By keeping the lamp as close as possible, leggyness is kept to a minimum.

When light shines on a garden, the leaves near the top of plants get more intense light than the leaves at the bottom. The top leaves shade the bottom leaves, absorbing light energy, making less light energy available to lower leaves. If the lower leaves do not receive enough light, they yellow and die. But, do not pick off perfectly good leaves so lower foliage gets more light! Tall 6-to-8 foot plants take longer to grow and yield more overall than shorter 4-foot plants, but the yield of flowers and foliage is about the same. The taller plants have large flowers on the top 3 to 4 feet and spindly buds near the bottom, due to lack of light. Tall plants tend to develop flower tops so heavy that the stem cannot support the weight, and they need to be tied up. Short plants support the weight of the tops better and flowers weigh more overall than leaves.

Annual flowers and vegetables should not be over waist-high before fruit and flowers set. Due to their high light requirements, these plants do not respond very well to weak light.

Several hundred two-week-old seedlings or clones may be huddled directly under a single HID. The young plants will need more space as they grow. Plants that are packed too close together sense the shortage of space and do not grow to their maximum potential. Leaves from one plant that shade another plant's leaves slow its development. It is very important to space young plants just far enough apart that their leaves do not touch. This will keep shading to a minimum and growth to a maximum. Check and alter the spacing every few days. Eight to 16 mature tomato plants will completely fill the space under one 1000-watt HID.

The **stadium method** is a very good way to get the most from an uneven garden profile. Tall plants go on the perimeter, while shorter plants crowd toward the center of the garden. The intensity of light all the plants receive is about the same, and tall plants do not shade shorter plants. See drawing below.

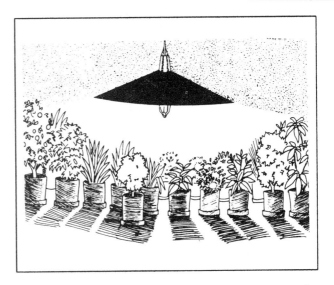

The stadium method places the tallest plants on the perimeter of the garden.

 RULE OF THUMB: Keep the HID 6 to 12 inches above garden. Tender clones, seedlings, and transplants require 24 to 36 inches. For other than fast-growing annuals, consult the "Plant Selection Guide" in Chapter Eleven.

The HID Lamp Family

Incandescent lamps create light by passing electricity through a very fine wire or filament. HID lamps make light by passing electricity through vaporized gas under high pressure. Fluorescent and low-pressure (LP) sodium lamps create light by passing electricity through gaseous vapor under low pressure. All of these principles are relatively simple.

The chart on page 20 shows various lamps with their lumen-per-watt conversion. This formula is used to measure the lamp's efficiency: the amount of lumens (light) produced in relation to the amount of watts (electricity) consumed. Note the high lumen-per-watt conversion of the halides and sodiums.

All the HID lamps work on the same principle, passing or do arcing electricity through gas or vapor, rather than using a tungsten filament, as household incandescent bulbs. The gas is inside a heat-resistant glass or ceramic arc tube, sealed under high pressure. The materials contained in the arc tube dictate the colors or spectrum the lamp will produce, except for the effect of the phosphor coating. Passing electricity through vaporized elements is an easy enough principle, but putting it into action requires a little technology.

HID lamps all work on the same principles; however, their starting requirements, line voltage, operating characteristics and physical shape are unique to each lamp.

CAUTION! Do not try to mix and match ballasts with lamps!

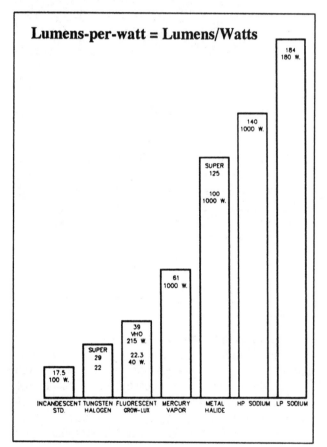

Lumens-per-watt = Lumens/Watts

The efficiency of the LP sodium lamp is misleading, because the largest wattage available is 180. One thousand watt HP sodium lamps are available and with a lumen-per-watt conversion of 140, the HP sodium is clearly the most efficient.

Just because a lamp fits a socket attached to a ballast does not mean that it will work properly in it. The wrong lamp plugged into the wrong ballast adds up to a burned out lamp!

RULE OF THUMB: Buy the entire HID system - ballast, lamp, socket, bulb and timer - all at the same time from a reputable supplier to ensure that the ballast and lamp belong together. Make sure to get a written guarantee from the dealer. The system should carry a complete guarantee for at least one year.

The electricity or line voltage (1) flows through the ballast (2). The ballast is the box that contains a capacitor (3) that provides a high, fast charge of electricity to start the lamps. Getting the electricity to flow between the electrodes (7) and (9) in the arc tube (10) requires a high-voltage charge or current. This current is sent through the starting mechanism of the lamp (5). In HP sodium lamps, the starting electrode and the operating electrode are one and the same.

The electricity is then arced or shot across the arc tube (10) from the starting electrode (6) to the operating electrode (9) at the other end of the arc tube. As soon as the arc is established and the gases vaporize, the arc jumps from the starting electrode to the operating electrodes (7) and (9). Once the electricity is flowing across the tube, the elements slowly vaporize into the discharge stream (8).

When the discharge stream (8) is working and the lamp warms up, the line voltage could run out of control, since there is an unrestricted flow of electricity between the two electrodes. The ballast (2) regulates this line voltage with a transformer, a wire coil wrapped around an iron core (4). By employing this core (4) the lamp is assured of having a constant and even supply of electricity.

About Ballasts

All HID's require ballasts. It is very important to buy the proper ballast for your HID. If possible, buy the assembled unit from a specialized retailer that advertises in *Growing Edge Magazine* listed in this book. Electrical supply and greenhouse supply stores also carry HID's. Buy component parts if you are low on capital and want to assemble the system yourself. However, you are not assured of saving any money.

Ballast components are manufactured by Advance, Jefferson, Sola and General Electric. Assembly instructions are in the form of a wiring diagram glued to the side of the transformer. The components consist of a transformer core, cooling capacitor, containing box and wire. Capacitor manufacturers are Cornell, General Electric, Duviler and Dayton. If you are not familiar with electrical component assembly and reading wiring diagrams, purchase the assembled ballast in a package containing the lamp and hood from one of the many HID distributors or retailers.

The metal halide ballast consists of (A) the transformer and (B) the capacitor.

Do not buy used parts from a junk yard or try to use a ballast if unsure of its capacity. The fact that a bulb fits a socket attached to a ballast mean all of the components are compatible. The best way to grow a miserable garden is to try to save money on the ballast.

Even though HID's have specific ballasting requirements, the ballasts have a good deal in common. The transformer consists of thin metal plates that are laminated together with a sticky, tar-like resin. This transformer core is then wrapped with wire. When operated at excessive temperatures or with poor ventilation, the resin becomes thin and the metal plates will begin to vibrate or hum super loud. This steady hum can be unnerving.

Ballasts are manufactured with a protective metal box. This outer shell safely contains the core, capacitor and wiring. Always use ballasts with all the wiring and necessary parts enclosed. Never use a ballast with exposed electrical connectors. Never build another box around a ballast. It will cause excessive heat and may even start a fire!

Ballasts operate at 90 to 150° F (65° C). Touch a strike-anywhere kitchen match to the side of the outer box to check if it is too hot. If the match lights, the ballast is too hot. It should be taken into the shop for repair before it creates an accident or burns out. Heat is the number one ballast destroyer!

120 volt - 208 volt
240 volt - 277 volt

A multi-tap ballast can be used as 110 or 220 volts. Single-tap ballasts must be either 110 volts or 220 volts.

Make sure the ballast has a handle on it. A small 400-watt halide ballast weighs about 30 pounds and a large 1000-watt HP sodium ballast tips the scales at about 55 pounds. This small, heavy box is very awkward to move with no handle.

Most ballasts sold by HID stores are set up for the 110-volt current found in all homes. Some may be ready for 220-volt service. It is usually easiest to use the regular 110-volt system because the outlets are more common. The 220-volt systems are normally used when several lamps are already taking up space on other 110-volt circuits. Changing all ballasts (except for Jefferson, which are manufactured either 110 or 220 volts and are not able to change) from 110 to 220 is a simple matter of moving one internal wire from the 110-volt brad to the 220 (208)-volt brad and changing the plug to a 220 type. Consult the wiring diagram in each ballast for specific instructions.

There is no difference in the electricity consumed by using either 110- or 220-volt systems. The 110-volt system draws about 9.5 amperes and an HID on a 220-volt current draws about 4.3 amperes. Both use the same amount of electricity! **Ohm's Power Law**: Volts X Amperes "" Watts.

This ballast is set up off the floor on a shelf to prevent excess water from leaking in the bottom.

More expensive ballasts are equipped with ventilation fans to maintain cool operation. A fan is not necessary unless there are many ballasts in a small room and ventilation is inadequate. Air vents allow a ballast to run cooler.

The vents should protect the internal parts and not be prone to letting water splash in.

Some industrial ballasts are sealed in fiberglass or a similar material to make them weatherproof. These ballasts are not recommended. They were designed for use outdoors where heat buildup is not a problem. Indoors, protecting the sealed unit from weather is not necessary, and could create excessive heat.

Ballasts that are 220-volts are easy to loop together. Up to four ballasts may be wired in a series circuit on a 220 volt, 30 ampere circuit. This is the most efficient way to use HID ballasts. There is less resistance for electricity when ballasts are wired in series. Less electricity is lost in transmission. I advise that only electricians try this relatively simple procedure. There is a lot more current flowing with more ballasts and grounding requirements increase. Any competent electrician should be able to loop ballasts together.

The ballast has a lot of electricity flowing through it. Do not place the ballast directly on a damp floor, or any floor that could get wet. Always place it up off the floor and protect it from possible moisture. The ballast should be suspended in the air or set on a shelf attached to the wall. It does not have to be very high, just far enough to keep it off a wet floor.

Ballast can be either remote or attached to the lamp. The remote ballast is the best for most indoor situations. It can be moved easily. laced near the floor, it can be used to radiate heat in a cool portion of the grow room. Place it outside if the room is too hot. Attached ballasts are fixed to the hood, require more overhead space, are very heavy, and create more heat around the lamp.

Some ballasts are manufactured with an attached timer. These units are very convenient, but the timer should be constructed of heavy-duty heat-resistant materials. If the timer is lightweight plastic, it could easily melt under the heat of the ballast.

A good ballast manufacturer will place a 10-ampere fuse inside the ballast. This is a double safeguard against electrical mishaps that destroy the lamp or cause a fire.

CAUTION! Do not touch the ballast when it is operating.

High Intensity Discharge Lamps

Artificial light from the High Intensity Discharge (HID) lamp family can be used to stimulate growth responses induced in plants by natural sunlight. This may be seen by comparing charts on HID spectral emission (pages 26 and 28) with the "Light Spectrum Chart" (page 15).

Metal halide lamps have shapely bulbous curves, while HP sodium lamps are more tubular in shape.

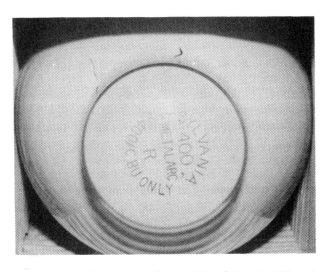

The lettering on the dome of the Sylvania 400 watt metal halide bulb lists a "C" for phosphor coated and "BU" for base up. The Westinghouse MS 1000/C/BU lamp is a super 1000-watt metal halide phosphor coated, base up bulb.The HID lamp family contains mercury vapor, metal halide and High Pressure (HP) sodium lamps.

The two most popular HID wattages are 400 and 1000. Value is the main reason. The 1000-watt system costs about 30 percent more than the 400-watt system, but is more efficient in its lumen-per-watt conversion and produces more than twice as much light. By employing a light mover, uniform light distribution is no longer a problem. The smaller 400-watt systems are great for a space that is 2- to 6-feet square, or a small greenhouse. The smaller 400-watt HID's are similar to the larger 1000-watt systems, only smaller. They produce less light and heat. Their color spectrum is almost identical to those of their big, 1000-watt brothers.

The 400-watt halides last about twice as long as the 1000-watt, but both have the same lumen maintenance curve!

Mercury Vapor Lamps

The mercury vapor lamp is the oldest and best-known member of the HID family. The HID principle was first used with the mercury vapor lamp around the turn of the century. But it was not until the mid-1930's that the mercury vapor lamp was really employed commercially on a large scale.

As the "Lumen-per-watt Chart" shows (page 21), the mercury vapor lamps produce only 60 lumens-per-watt. The spectral energy distribution of the mercury vapor does not fulfill the light requirements outlined by the "Photosynthetic Response Chart" (page 15). The mercury vapor is a poor lamp for horticulture. Not only is it expensive to operate, but it produces most color in areas that are not helpful to plant growth.

The old mercury vapor lamps produce light by arcing electricity through mercury and a little argon gas is used for starting. They come in sizes from 40 to 1000-watts. They have fairly good lumen maintenance and a fairly long life. Most wattages last up to three years at 18-hour daily operation.

The mercury vapor usually requires a separate ballast; however, there are a few low wattage bulbs that have self-contained ballast. All too often these ballasts are scrounged from junk yards or who-knows-where and used in place of halide or HP sodium ballasts. People who use or try to modify these ballasts for use with another HID have all kinds of problems and still have to buy the proper ballast in the end. Remember, trying to save money on a ballast usually costs more in produce that was not realized.

In summary, the mercury vapor lamp produces a color spectrum that is not as efficient as the halide or HP sodium for indoor cultivation. It is not the lamp to use if you want any kind of garden at all! Gardeners who have used them paid more for electricity and their gardens yielded much less.

Metal Halide Lamps

The metal halide HID lamp is the most efficient source of artificial white light available to the horticulturist today. It comes in 175, 250, 400, 1000, and 1500-watt sizes. They may be either clear or phosphor-coated, and all require a special ballast. Most gardeners do not consider using the 175- or 250-watt halides. The 1500-watt halide is also avoided due to its relatively short (2000 to 3000 hours) life and incredible heat output. Most gardeners prefer the 1000-watt halide and those with small growing areas or low-light greenhouses the 400-watt.

Metal halides are either clear or phosphor coated.

Three major metal halide manufacturers are General Electric (Multivapor), Sylvania (Metalarc), and Phillips/Westinghouse (Metal Halide). Each manufacturer has a super version of the halide. The Super Metalarc, the High-Output Multivapor and The Super Metal Halide fit the standard halide ballast and fixture. They produce about 25 percent more lumens than the standard halides. These super halides cost about $10 more than the standard, but are well worth the extra money.

The clear halides are the most commonly used by indoor gardeners. The clear bulb offers the brightest white available. It supplies the most lumens of the best possible spectrum for plant growth. The clear halide works well for seedling, vegetative, and flower growth.

Phosphor-coated 1000-watt halides emit more diffused light. They are easy on the eyes, emitting less ultraviolet light than clear halides. They produce the same initial lumens and about 4,000 fewer lumens than the standard halide, and have a slightly different color spectrum. Phosphor-coated halides emit more yellows, less blue and less ultraviolet light. Some gardeners prefer the phosphor-coated halide to the HP sodium for both vegetative growth and flowering, saying it is the best all-round bulb.

The 1000-watt super clear and super phosphor-coated halides are the most common halides used indoors. Compare energy distribution charts and the lumen output of all three lamps to decide which lamp offers the most desirable characteristics for your garden. Typically, the home gardener starts with the 1000-watt Super Metalarc (Sylvania), High-Output Multivapor (G.E.) or Super Metal Halide (Westinghouse).

Construction and Operation

Metal halide lamps produce light by passing or arcing electricity through vaporized argon gas, mercury, thorium iodide, sodium iodide and scandium iodide within the quartz arc tube (1).
At the end of the arc tube is a heat reflecting coating (2) to control temperature during operation. Spring supports in the neck (4) and dome (3) of the outer bulb or envelope (5) mount the arc tube frame (9) in place. The bimetal shorting switch (6) closes during lamp operation, preventing voltage drop between the main electrode (7) and the starting electrode (8). Most bulbs are equipped with a resistor (10) that keeps the bulb from shattering under temperature stress. The outer bulb functions as a protective jacket. It contains the arc tube and starting mechanism, keeping them in a constant environment as well as absorbing ultraviolet radiation. Protective goggles that filter out ultraviolet rays are a good idea if you spend much time in the grow room.

Diagram of a metal halide lamp.

but once, the system is seasoned, clear white light appears.

If a power surge occurs and the lamp goes out, or if the lamp is turned off, it will take 5 to 15 minutes for the lamp to restart. The gases inside the arc tube must cool before restarting. If the lamp is on a timer, it will restart automatically. There is no need to turn the timer on or off manually.

When the lamp is started, incredible voltage is necessary for the initial ionization process to take place. Turning the lamp on and off more than once a day causes unnecessary stress on the HID system and will shorten its life.

Burning positions of BU metal halide lamps. Metal halide "HOR" lamps can be burned in a horizontal position.

The five halogens include the elements fluorine, chlorine, bromine, iodine and astatine. iagram of a metal halide lamp.

CAUTION! If outer bulb shatters, turn off (unplug) the lamp immediately. Do not look at or get near the lamp until it cools down. When the outer bulb breaks, it is no longer able to absorb ultraviolet radiation. This radiation is very harmful and will burn skin and eyes if exposed. Be careful!

Initial vaporization takes place in the gap between the main electrode (7) and the starting electrode (8) when a high starting voltage is applied. When there is enough ionization, electricity will arc between the main electrodes (7). As the lamp warms up, the metal iodide additives begin to enter the arc stream. After they are in their proper concentrations in the arc tube, the characteristic bright white light is emitted. This process takes about 3 to 5 minutes.

Note: The metal halide arc system is very complex and requires a seasoning period of 100 hours operation for all of its components to stabilize. At first the colors produced by the bulb may vary,

Metal halides have very good lumen maintenance and a long life. The decline in lumen output over the lamp's life is very gradual. The average life of a halide is about 12,000 hours - almost two years of daily operation at 18 hours. Many will last even longer. The lamp has reached the end of its life when it fails to start or come up to full brilliance. This is usually caused by deterioration of lamp electrodes over time, loss of transmission of the arc tube from blackening, or shifts in the chemical balance of the metals in the arc tube. I do not advise waiting until the bulb is burned out before changing it. An old bulb is inefficient and costly. Replace bulbs about every 12 to 18 months or 6,500 hours. Electrode deterioration is greatest during starting, and is usually the reason for the end of lamp life. Do not start the halide more than once a day, and use a timer!

The halide may produce a stroboscopic (flashing) effect. The light will appear bright, then dim, bright, dim, etc. This flashing is the result of the arc being extinguished 120 times every second. Illumination usually remains constant, but it may pulsate a little. This is normal and nothing to worry about.

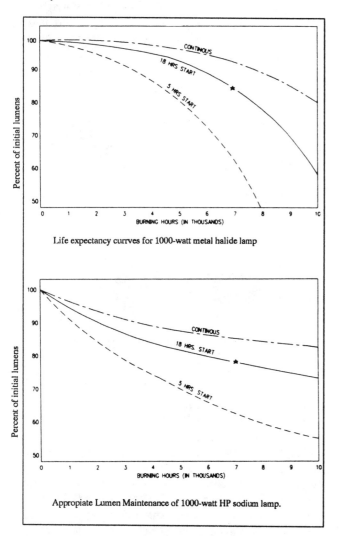

Life expectancy currves for 1000-watt metal halide lamp

Appropiate Lumen Maintenance of 1000-watt HP sodium lamp.

Successful gardeners change the bulb before it burns out. This is about every 12 to 18 months or 6,500 hours. This ensures maximum light intensity.

Metal halides operate most efficiently in a vertical +/- 15⁰ position (see Diagram A). When operated in positions other than +/- 15⁰ of vertical, lamp wattage, lumen output, and life will decrease; the arc bends, creating non-uniform heating of the arc tube wall. The result is less efficient operation, and shorter life.

Energy distribution of 1000-watt phosphor coated metal halide

Spectral Energy Distribution of 1000-watt metal halide lamp.

Halide Ballasts

Read "About Ballasts" pages 21-22. The ballast for a 1000-watt halide will operate standard, clear, or phosphor-coated, or super, clear and phosphor-coated halides on a 110- or 220-volt current. The bulbs can be either "BU" or "HOR". A different ballast is required for 400-watt halides; it will operate all 400-watt halides: super or standard, "BU", or "HOR", clear or phosphor-coated.

The ballasts must be specifically designed for the 400- or 1000-watt halides, since their starting and operating requirements are unique.

High Pressure Sodium Lamps

The most impressive fact about the 1000-watt high pressure sodium vapor lamp is that it produces 140,000 initial lumens. That's one brilliant light! The HP sodium is also the most efficient HID lamp available.

It is available in 35, 50, 70, 100, 150, 200, 250, 310, 400 and 1000 wattages. All, may be either clear or phosphor-coated, except the 200- and 1000-watt bulbs (which are available only clear). All HP sodium vapor lamps have their own unique ballast. HP sodium lamps are manufactured by G.E. (Lucalox), Sylvania (Lumalux) and Westinghouse (Ceramalux). The Ceramalux has a color-corrected spectrum. It produces a little more blue than other HP sodiums. Iwasaki produces a very high quality HP sodium bulb. In fact, the Iwasaki bulbs are known by most gardeners as the top of the line. They produce more blue light than most other HP sodium lamps. The Son Agro lamp manufactured by Phillips produces 30 percent more blue light than their Son-T-Agro lamp. This HP sodium lamp was developed specifically for Dutch greenhouse growers that use lights.

Most gardeners find the best value is with the 1000-watt HP sodium rather than the 400-watt.

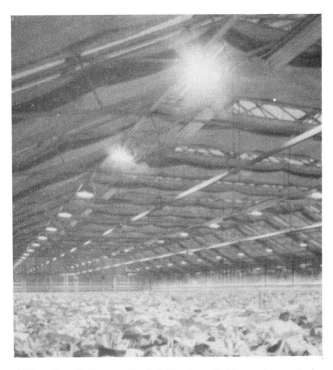

HP sodium bulbs are the brightest available and operate in any position, 360º.

The HP sodium lamp emits an orange-like glow that is sometimes compared to that of the harvest sun. The color spectrum is highest in the yellow, orange and red end. These colors promote flower production and stem elongation.

Light from the red end of the spectrum stimulates floral hormones within the plant, promoting more flower production. When using an HP sodium lamp, flower volume and weight may increase by 20 percent or more, depending on variety of seed and growing conditions. Many gardeners, using a 10-by-10-foot room, will retain the 1000-watt halide and add a 1000-watt sodium during flowering. This not only more than doubles available light, but increases the red end of the spectrum, causing flowers to form and grow like crazy. This 1:1 ratio (one halide and one HP sodium) is a popular combination for flowering. But many growers report the same or better results using *only* HP sodium lamps.

The HP sodium is the only practical lamp to use in a greenhouse. Since the sun provides all the blue light necessary, the HP sodium is used during low-light hours and during total darkness.

Construction and Operation

The HP sodium lamp produces light by passing electricity through vaporized sodium and mercury within an arc tube (1). A small quantity of xenon gas, used for starting, is also included in the arc tube.

The HP sodium lamp is totally different from the metal halide in its physical, electrical and color spectrum characteristics. An electronic starter works with the magnetic component of the ballast to supply a short, high-voltage pulse. This electrical pulse vaporizes the xenon gas and initiates the starting process, which takes 3 to 4 minutes. Electricity passes or arcs between the two main electrodes (6) and (7). If the lamp is turned off, or power surge occurs and the lamp goes out, the gases in the tube will usually need to cool 3 to 15 minutes before restarting is possible. As with the metal halides, if the HP sodium is on a timer, it will restart automatically.

Like the metal halide, the HP sodium has a two bulb construction, with an outer protective bulb (2), and inner arc tube (1). The arc tube's frame (5) is mounted by spring supports in the dome (3), and neck (4). The outer bulb or jacket protects the arc tube from damage and contains a vacuum, reducing heat loss from the arc tube. The sodium, mercury and xenon gas are contained within the arc tube and have a constant operating temperature, and the lamp may be operated in any position (360º). However, most growers prefer to hang the lamp overhead in a vertical operating position.

Diagram of a high pressure (HP) sodium lamp.

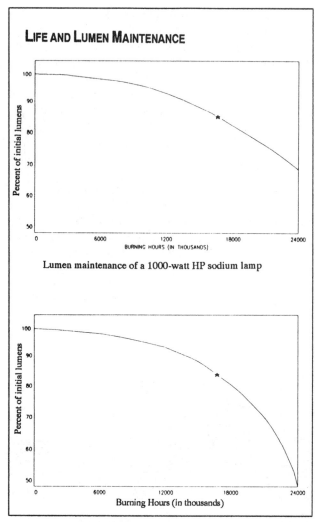

Lumen maintenance of a 1000-watt HP sodium lamp

Mortality curves of a 1000-watt HP sodium lamp show a long lamp life. For best results, change the HP Sodium bulb after 15,000 hours of operation.

Life and Lumen Maintenance

HP sodium lamps have the longest life and best lumen maintenance of all HID lamps. Eventually the sodium bleeds out through the arc tube; over a long period of daily use, the ratio of sodium to mercury changes, causing the voltage in the arc to rise. Finally the arc tube's operating voltage will rise higher than the ballast is able to sustain. At this point, the lamp will start, warm up to full intensity, then go out. This sequence is then repeated over and over, signaling the end of the lamp's life. The life of a 1000-watt HP sodium lamp will be about 24,000 hours, or five years operating at 12 hours a day. As with other HID's, HP sodiums should be replaced before the end of their rated life.

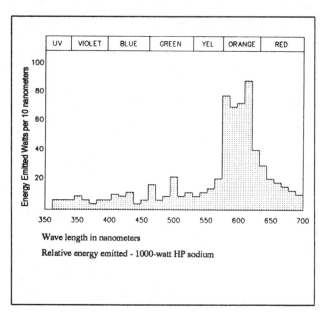

Relative energy emitted - 1000-watt HP sodium

HP Sodium Ballasts

Read "About Ballasts," pages 21-22. A special ballast is required specifically for the 400- or 1000-watt HP sodium lamp. The lamp has unique operating voltages and currents during start up and operation. These voltages and currents do not correspond to similar wattages of other HID lamps. As with the halide ballast, to save money and time I recommend purchasing it from an HID lamp store rather than in a component kit.

Never remove a warm lamp. The heat makes them expand in the socket. A hot bulb is more difficult to remove and must be forced. Vaseline or a special electrical lubricant may be smeared lightly (it takes only a dash) around the mogul socket base to facilitate screwing it in and out.

Always keep the bulb clean. Wait for it to cool and wipe it off every 2-4 weeks with a clean cloth. Dirt will lower lumen output.

Store HID's that are not being used in the same box they came in.

HID bulbs are tough and durable. They survive being shipped many miles by uncaring carriers. Once the bulb has been used a few hours, the arc tube blackens and the internal parts become somewhat brittle. After a bulb has been used several hundred hours, a good bump will substantially shorten its life and lessen its luminescence.

Conversion Bulbs

Conversion bulbs are available for metal halide ballasts. The conversion bulb operates on a metal halide system, but produces a light spectrum very similar to the HP sodium bulb. The outer bulb looks like a metal halide. The internal arc tube is very similar to that of a HP sodium. A small starter (ignightor) is located at the base of the arc tube.

The bulbs are available in either 360-watt or 940-watt sizes. The 360-watt conversion bulb operates on a 400-watt metal halide system. The 940-watt conversion bulb runs on a 1000-watt metal halide system. Since the bulb operates at a lower wattage, it is not quite as bright as a HP sodium bulb. runs at The price of the conversion bulbs is slowly becoming affordable. The price of a conversion bulb is more economical than buying a complete HP sodium system. The conversion bulb offers an excellent value to gardeners that only have one metal halide system.

Conversion bulbs convert a metal halide system into a HP sodium system.

Disposing of an HID Lamp.

Please read the following rules of disposal before laying a faithful HID to rest:

One: Break the lamp outdoors in a container. Hit it a couple of inches from the base with a hard object. Take care to avoid shattering glass, as the bulbs are under vacuum.

Two: The lamps contain materials that are harmful to the skin, so contact should be avoided and protective clothing should be used.

Three: Once the lamp is broken, place it in a plastic bag, then throw it away.

Four: Under no conditions place the bulb in a fire.

Fluorescent Lamps

Until HID's were developed, fluorescent light was the most efficient and widely used form of artificial light available to the indoor gardener. Some fluorescent lamps boast a spectrum almost identical to that of the sun, but they are not bright enough to grow high-light plants efficiently.

Today, these lamps are most efficiently used as a light source to root cuttings and grow low-light plants. Fluorescent lamps are manufactured in long glass tubes or circle-line tubes, and illuminate in many commercial and residential buildings. They are available in a wide variety of sizes: lengths of 18 inches, 24, 36, 48, 72, and 96 inches, and standard circline-tube diameters of 8, 14, 12, and 16 inches. Longer tubes are better to use than short ones since there is a light loss at the ends of tubes. The 4-foot and 8-foot tubes and the easiest to handle and most readily available. However, 8-foot tubes are easily damaged in shipping. Buy 8-foot tubes at a retail store rather than via mail order.

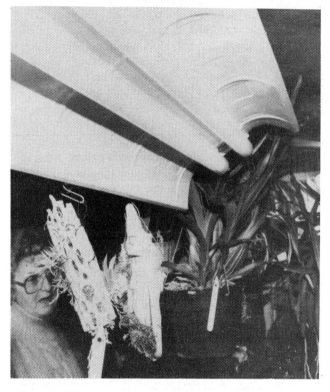

This orchid grower uses fluorescent lamps to help illuminate her greenhouse.

Fluorescent tubes are available in several wattages or outputs. Ballasts also operate at different wattages. Both tubes and ballasts are made by several companies. The standard or regular tubes use about 10 watts per linear foot. A 4-foot tube uses about 40 watts, 8-foot, 80 watts, etc. High-Output (HO) tubes use about 50 percent more watts-per-linear-foot and emit about 40 percent more light than the standard. These fluorescents require a special ballast and end caps. Very High Output (VHO) use almost three times as much electricity, and produce more than twice as much light as the standard fluorescent. VHO fluorescents are more expensive and more difficult to find. VHO tubes also require a special ballast. They can be ordered from the manufacturer or purchased from the wholesaler.

Fluorescent lamps are an excellent light source to root cuttings. They supply cool, diffused light in the proper color spectrum to promote root growth. The VHO tubes are more expensive, but are preferred for their high lumen output. None-the-less, if low on capital, a gardener may use any fluorescent lamp to root cuttings. The only drawback to using the less luminous standard or HO fluorescents is that cuttings may take a few days longer to root. Fluoescents, like HID's, diminish in intensity with distance from the light source. Since fluorescents produce much less light than HID's, they must be very close 2 to 4 inches to the plants for best results.

In many cases, as when there are many plant varieties and ages of plants under a fluorescent, it is easier to retain the lamp at one overhead level. Move the plants closer to the lamp by placing them on a block to elevate then.

A few gardeners hang extra fluorescent lamps with HID's to increase light intensity. This works well, but I have found fluorescent lamps to be more trouble than they are worth for anything but rooting cuttings and growing low-light plants. Fluorescent tubes are most effective when mounted above plants if they are the only source of light. When tubes are placed vertically around plants, they do not promote straight, even growth. If used with bright halides, fluorescents can be used as side lighting for lower leaves, but it is a difficult job to mount the fluorescent fixtures close enough to the plants to do any good. Fluorescent fixtures can also shade plants from HID light and generally get in the way.

Fluorescent lamps have a wide variety of spectrums. Sylvania makes the Gro-Lux and the Wide Spectrum Gro-Lux. The Standard Gro-Lux is the lamp to use for starting clones or seedlings. It is designed to be used as the only source of light, having the full spectrum necessary for photosynthesis and chlorophyll production. The Wide Spectrum Gro-Lux is designed to supplement natural light and covers the blue to far red regions. Westinghouse makes the Agro-Light, which produces a very similar spectrum to the sun. Warm White and Cool White bulbs used together, make excellent lamps to root clones.

Power Twist or Power Groove lamps offer additional lumens in the same amount of linear space. The deep, wide grooves in the tube give more glass surface area and more light output.

Fluorescent bulbs and fixtures are relatively inexpensive. Two, 4-foot bulbs and a fixture will usually cost from $20 to $30. Clones root best with 18 hours of fluorescent light.

Side mount reflectors have a partition between the light tubes. This partition eliminates light loss that occurs when the tubes are side by side. The side mount fixtures offer the best value. If you unable to buy fixtures with this partition, you can easily construct one from stiff white paper and tape it to the fixture.

Light spectrum charts of various fluorescent lamps.

Duro-Lite Fluorescent Lamp

Standard Grow-Lux Fluorescent Lamp

Warm White Fluorescent Lamp

Cool White Fluorescent Lamp

Construction and Operation

Like the HID family, fluorescent lamps require an appropriate fixture, containing a ballast (much smaller than the HID ballast) and the ordinary 110- or 120-volt house current. The fixture is usually integrated into the reflective hood. There are several types of fixtures. Some have one pin on each end; others are two pin types. If purchasing new tubes, make sure the bulb fits the fixture. The fixture may contain one, two or four tubes.

The ballast, which is contained in the fixture, radiates almost all of the heat produced by the system. The ballast is located far enough away from standard tubes that plants can actually touch them without being burned. VHO tubes may burn tender plants if they get too close.

The ballast or transformer regulates electricity. Most ballasts and fixtures are for use with standard 40- or 80-watt tubes. Special ballasts are required for VHO fluorescent tubes. The operating requirements of VHO lamps are greater, due to the increase in current, than for standard fluorescent lamps. I advise ordering the VHO ballast, fixture and tubes at the same time as a package and from a reputable supplier.

The ballast reduces the current in the tube to the operating voltage required by a particular lamp. The ballast will normally last 10 to 12 years. Used fluorescent fixtures (unlike used mercury vapor ballasts) are generally acceptable. The end of life is usually accompanied by smoke and a disagreeable chemical odor. When the ballast burns out, remove it (or take the entire fixture to the nearest electrical supply store) and buy a new one to replace it. Be very careful if the ballast has brown slime or sludge on or around it. This sludge could possibly contain PCB's. If the ballast contains the sludge, throw it away at an approved dump site. Most modern fluorescent lamps are self-starting, but older fluorescents require a special starter. This starter may be integrated into the body of the fixture and hidden from view, or be a small metal tube (about an inch in diameter and half an inch long), located at the end of the fixture on the underside. The latter starters are replaceable; the former require a trip to the electrical store.

If the ballast creates too much heat, remove it from the fixture and place it in a remote location. Just splice the wires. Secure the remote ballast away from water and excessive heat to prevent damage.

Most electrical supply stores are able to test starters. If your fluorescent fixture does not work, and you are not well versed in fluorescent troubleshooting, take it to the nearest electric store to ask for advice. Make sure they test each component and tell you why it should be replaced.

The tubular fluorescent glass bulb is coated on the inside with phosphor. The mix of phosphorescent chemicals in the coating and the gases contained within determine the spectrum of colors emitted by the lamp. The bulb contains a blend of inert gases: argon, neon or krypton and mercury vapor, sealed under low pressure.

Electricity arcs between the two electrodes, located at each end of the tube, stimulating the phosphor to emit light. The light emission is strongest near the center of the tube and somewhat less at the ends. If rooting just a few cuttings, place them under the center of the fixture for best results.

Once the fluorescent is turned on, it will take a few seconds for the bulb to warm up before an arc can be struck through the tube. Fluorescent lamps blacken with age, losing intensity. I recommend replacing bulbs when they reach 70 percent of their stated service life listed on the package or label. A flickering light is about to burn out and should be replaced.

Life expectancy ranges from 9,000 hours (a little more than a year at 18 hours daily operation) with VHO tubes to 18,000 hours (2 1/2 years at 18 hours daily operation) with the standard tubes.

Change fluorescent lamps every 9 to 12 months. Use a grease pencil to mark the date that you install any light. Mark the bulb or fixture near the end or base.

Other Lamps

Incandescent Lamps

The incandescent lamp is the electric lamp invented by Thomas Edison. Light is produced by sending electricity through the filament, a very fine wire inside the bulb. The filament resists the flow of electricity, heating it to incandescence (causing it to glow). Incandescent bulbs work on ordinary household current and require no ballast. Filaments may be of many shapes and sizes, but are nearly always made of tough, heat-resistant tungsten. They come in a wide range of wattages and constructions for special applications.

Most lamps used in homes for Christmas trees, interior lighting, and refrigerators are incandescent lamps.

There are many types of incandescent lamps. They usually use a tungsten filament with a glass bulb construction and threaded base that fits household sockets. The bulb is usually under a vacuum, or contains some type of gas to minimize wear on the filament.

Light spectrum chart of an incandescent lamp.

Most incandescents have a spectrum in the far red end, but there are some incandescent grow lamps that have a more balanced spectrum. Incandescent lamps are expensive to operate and produce so few lumens-per-watt that they are not worth using. They are most efficiently used as a source of bottom or soil heat for clones rooting under cool fluorescent. A few gardeners use incandescents during flowering to help promote more and heavier flowers.

Tungsten Halogen Lamps

The tungsten halogen lamp was originally called the iodine quartz lamp. The outer tube is made of heat-resistant quartz and the main gas inside the quartz tube was iodine, one of the five halogens

There are several variations of the quartz halogen or quartz tungsten lamp. Today bromine, also one of the halogens, is used most often in the lamps, so the name halogen covers all of the gases in the arc tube. Tungsten lamps are very similar to incandescents. They electricity flows through a tungsten wire filament sealed in bulb. They are very expensive to operate. Their lumen-per-watt output is very low. Tungsten halogens, like incandescents, run on 110-volt current and require no ballast. They are as inefficient to operate as incandescents (See "Lumen-per-watt Chart", page 21). Their color spectrum is in the far red end. Only 10 to 15 percent is in the visible spectrum.

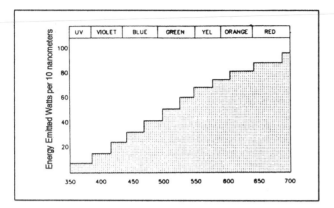

Light spectrum chart of a tungsten halogen lamp.

LP Sodium Lamps

Low-Pressure (LP) sodium lamps are available in 55, 90, 135 and 180 wattages. Their lumen-per-watt conversion is the highest of all lamps on the market today. More careful inspection of the color spectrum chart above shows that it is monochromatic, or produces light only in one very narrow portion of the spectrum, at 589 nanometers (nm). The LP sodium lamp emits a yellow glow. Colors are not distinguished and appear as tones.

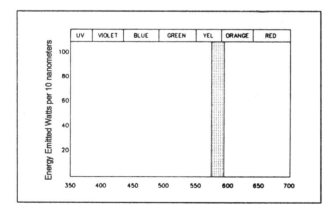

Light spectrum chart of a LP sodium lamp.

LP sodium lamps are supplied by Phillips/Westinghouse. Their main use has been for security, street and warehouse lighting.

Each wattage requires its own unique ballast and fixture. The ballast or transformer regulates electric current and is located inside the fixture. The fixture for a 180 watt lamp is just a little larger than a fixture for two 40 watt 4-foot fluorescent tubes.

Phillips/Westinghouse is the only supplier of LP sodium lamps. The ballast and fixture for a LP sodium system costs about $200. As with other lamps, I advise purchasing the lamp, ballast and fixture from a reputable supplier together in the same package.

The LP sodium must be used with a metal halide lamp to stimulate photosynthesis and chlorophyll synthesis. LP sodium lamps work well for side lighting or in areas with high electrical rates.

This lamp has the unique quality of maintaining 100 percent of its lumen output throughout its life. There is no gradual decrease in the lumen output over time as with other discharge lamps. The LP sodium lamp will burn out all at once, at about 18,000 hours.

The basic design of the LP sodium lamp is essentially the same as it was when first introduced to the market in 1932. Like HID lamps, the LP sodium has a two-bulb construction. The arc tube is made of lime borate glass and contains a mixture of neon, argon and pure sodium metal. The neon and argon begin to glow after electricity enters the arc tube.

As the gas mixture gives off increasing amounts of heat, the sodium metal, which is still in the solid form, begins to vaporize. A yellowish glow is soon emitted from the vaporized sodium.

Fixtures can be lightweight plastic due to low outside bulb temperatures. The LP sodium lamp conserves energy by keeping heat inside the lamp. A special reflective coating on the outer tube allows light to pass outward while heat remains inside. A vacuum is formed between the outer and inner tubes, retaining even more heat.

To ensure long life of the lamp, it should be operated horizontally. Do not let it operate at more than 20 percent +/- off horizontal.

Pure sodium metal will react with air or water and explode. There is about one gram of sodium in a 180 watt LP sodium lamp - not enough to cause a big explosion, but enough to warrant careful handling. When disposing of an LP sodium bulb, place it in a dry, plastic garbage can and break it.

Reflective Light

Reflective light also increases light intensity by as much as 30 percent. A large white 4-foot reflective hood over the lamp and flat white walls will triple the growing area.

EXAMPLE: Using a 1000-watt super metal halide with a small, 2-foot hood and no reflective walls and ceiling, the effective growing area is only 36 square feet. When a large 4-foot white reflective hood and flat white walls and ceiling are added, effective growing area is increased to 100 square feet.

Reflective hoods come in all shapes and sizes. The main features to look for in a hood are the size, the reflective ability and the specific application. Parabolic dome reflectors work very well. The light has a good chance to spread out and not be reflected around within the walls of the hood. These hoods are very popular because they are inexpensive and provide the maximum amount of reflection for the least amount of money.

Artificial light fades fast. The farther away from the light source (bulb), the less light available. This is the most critical factor when using artificial light.

The farther the light travels from the source, the less intense it is. If this light must be reflected, the closer the reflector is to the bulb, the more intense the light will be when it is reflected. For example, If the reflector is one foot from the bulb, the light that is reflected will be four times more intense than if the reflector were two feet away. Look at the "Light and Distance Chart" on page 16.

To prove all these simple premises, we constructed a black room to measure light. The room is of simple design. It is 10' X 10' square and the walls are painted flat black. The floor is covered with black tar paper. On the floor, on 12-inch centers, dots are marked to form a matrix. Each of the four walls has one foot increments marked. The flat black paint and black tar paper floor reflect a maximum of 3 percent light. This small percentage of reflection will facilitate consistent light measurements.

There were two lamps used in this test, a 1000-watt clear super metal halide and a 1000-watt HP sodium. The bottom of each bulb was hung at a distance of 3 feet from the floor. The lamps were warmed up for an hour before any measurements were taken.

A light reading was taken at each square foot of the matrix on the floor. The footcandle reeding was recorded next to a corresponding point on a chart. To complete the charts, a line was drawn connecting all of the dots on the matrix that have a value of 500, 1,000, 1,500 and 2,000 footcandles. The charts are very interesting and demonstrate where the high-light and low-light plants should be placed.

The charts show that a 40-inch parabolic reflector delivers 24 percent more light than a 45-inch cone-shaped reflector.

Light distribution of a 1000-watt super metal halide in footcandles of a 45-inch cone-shaped reflector.

Light distribution of a 1000-watt super metal halide in footcandles of a 40-inch parabola reflector.

The tests above compare a 45-inch cone-shaped reflector and a 40-inch parabolic dome reflector.

Horizontal reflectors are much more efficient than reflectors requiring the lamp to burn vertically. Turning a lamp horizontally increases light output substantially. By turning the lamp on it's side, the arc tube is parallel with the ground. All of the light comes out of the arc tube. When the arc tube is already horizontal, half of the light it produces shines directly on plants. Only half of the light needs to be reflected. When the arc tube is in a vertical position, light is emitted out the sides of the arc tube. This light must be reflected downward before it is of any value to plants.

The charts show that a compact horizontal reflector delivers 40 percent more light than a 45-inch cone-shaped reflector. The 40-inch parabolic reflector delivers 19 percent more light than a 45-inch cone-shaped reflector.

The hoods can be covered with white paint or constructed from a reflective. First and foremost, they should be made
of a material that is lightweight, since they will be hanging from the ceiling. The hood should have a heat vent outlet around the bulb so that it will not collect heat. Excessive heat around the bulb could cause premature burn-out.

The hoods can be made of galvanized steel, polished or painted aluminum. The color is usually flat white, but some companies paint them glossy white (see discussion below on flat white paint). Sheet metal hoods tend to be much less expensive than aluminum or stainless steel; But, sheet metal is heavy. The other differences in reflective quality are similar to the differences between flat white paint and reflective mylar, discussed later. Polished aluminum hoods scratch easily and are expensive.

For maximum reflection, paint the inside of the reflector with titanium white paint. Tests we completed showed titanium white reflectors produce 5-10 percent more light.

The 4-foot parabolic hoods are usually manufactured in 9 parts. The smaller size facilitates shipping and handling. The customer assembles the hood with small screws and nuts.

HP sodium lamps mounted horizontally use a small, very effective hood for greenhouse culture. The hood is mounted just a few inches over the long horizontal HP sodium so that all the light is reflected down toward the plant beds but the small hood creates a minimum shadow. One manufacturer's hood for its HP sodium has a protective glass covering to protect the lamp from water spray when irrigating.

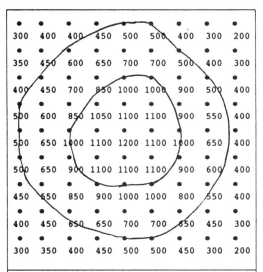

Light distribution of a 1000-watt HP lamp in footcandles of a 45-inch cone-shaped reflector.

Light distribution of a 1000-watt HP sodium lamp in footcandles, of a 40-inch parabola reflector.

The tests above compare a 45-inch cone-shaped reflector, a 40-inch parabolic dome reflector and a compact horizontal reflector.

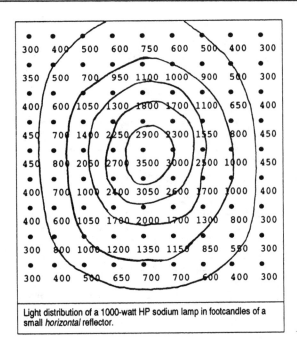

300	400	500	600	750	600	500	400	300
350	500	700	950	1100	1000	900	500	300
400	600	1050	1300	1800	1700	1100	650	400
450	700	1400	2250	2900	2300	1550	800	450
450	800	2050	2700	3500	3000	2500	1000	450
400	700	1000	2400	3050	2600	1700	1000	400
400	600	1050	1700	2000	1700	1300	800	300
300	800	1000	1200	1350	1150	850	550	300
300	400	500	650	700	700	600	400	300

Light distribution of a 1000-watt HP sodium lamp in footcandles of a small *horizontal* reflector.

The reflective hood on this horizontal 400-watt metal halide lamp from Hydrofarm spreads the light evenly.

This hood from Diamond Lights is typical of the efficient horizontal reflectors.

One option is to remove the reflective hood if the garden is too tall. With no hood, the lamp burns cooler, and the white ceiling provides some reflection. If the lamp is too close to the ceiling (less than 24 inches) install a non-flammable heat shield to protect the ceiling. See instruction Number Two in "Setting Up the Lamp," pages 44-46.

White, reflective walls should be 12 inches or less from the plants for optimum reflection. Ideally, the walls should be moved around the plants. This way, the walls always provide the optimum amount of reflection. The easiest way to install mobile walls is to hang the lamp near the corner of a room. Use the two walls in the corner as reflective walls. Fabricate two outside walls that are mobile. They will need to be fabricated out of light plywood, sheet rock, or white visqueen plastic.

Hanging white visqueen plastic is a great way to white out a room. People use it for several reasons. White visqueen is inexpensive, expandable, removable and reusable. It may also be used to construct walls. This is very handy when a gardener wants to partition off one or several rooms. The walls can expand as the garden grows. The plastic is waterproof, so it may be used on the walls as well as the floor. White visqueen is easy to work with. It may be cut with scissors or a knife, stapled, nailed or taped. Generally, people hang the plastic sheets wrapped around a 1-by-2's nailed to the ceiling. The white visqueen actually forms a mobile wall around the garden. It is easy to keep the walls close to the plants for optimum reflection. To make the white walls opaque, hang black visqueen on the outside. The dead air space between the two types of visqueen increases insulation.

The only disadvantages of white visqueen plastic are that it is not as reflective as flat white paint, it may get brittle after a couple of years of use under an HID lamp, and it is difficult to find at retail outlets.

Whitewash is an inexpensive alternative to white paint. It is a little messy to apply, and it is thin, so several coats will have to be applied. If fungus or moisture is a problem, like the kind found on wet concrete basement walls, the mess is worth the trouble. For mixing directions, see page 52.

This innovative HID reflective hood is manufactured by Green Air Products. The hood stays less than 100° F, even on hot summer days!

Using flat white paint is one of the simplest, least expensive, most efficient ways to create optimum reflection. Artist's white or titanium white paint is more expensive, but very reflective. It is recommended for reflective hoods. Semi-gloss white is not quite as reflective as flat white, but it is much easier to wash and keep clean. A gallon of good flat white paint costs $15 to $20. One gallon should be enough to "white out" the average grow room. Use a primer to prevent bleed through of stains or if walls are rough and unpainted. The vent fan should be installed before painting. Fumes can cause headaches and nausea.

Why is flat white so reflective? When light shines on a green object, green pigment in the object absorbs all colors but green from the spectrum and the green light is reflected. This is why we see the color green. Flat white contains little or no light-absorbing pigment. Flat white essentially absorbs no light; it is almost all reflected, except for a small amount that somehow gets lost. Flat white is whiter and reflects better than glossy white. Glossy white is manufactured with more light-absorbing varnish. The glossy surface lends itself to bright spots and glare. Flat white contains less varnish and inhibits the path of reflective light much less. It also has a mat texture, actually providing more reflective surface.

Reflective mylar provides one of the most reflective surfaces possible. It looks like a very thin mirror. Unlike light absorbing paint, reflective mylar reflects almost all light. It is simply taped or tacked to the wall. The trick to setting it up is to make it lay down flat against the wall. When it is loose or wavy, light is reflected poorly.

Aluminum foil is one of the worst reflective surfaces possible. The foil always crinkles up, reflecting light in the wrong directions, actually wasting light. It also reflects more ultraviolet rays than other surfaces. Take a look at the reflective chart. Aluminum foil is not very reflective!

REFLECTIVE CHART

MATERIAL	Percentage of Light Reflected
Reflective Mylar	90 - 95
Flat white paint	85 - 93
Semi-gloss white	75 - 80
Flat yellow	70 - 80
Aluminum foil	70 - 75
Black	less than 10

More Growing Light for Less Money

There are several ways of getting a more even distribution of light in the garden. Use several 400-watt HID's, installing side lighting, or rotate the plants. The most efficient way is to replicate the movement of the sun through the sky. This is done two basic ways. Both methods move the lamp back and forth overhead so it covers more area.

One: The plants get more even distribution of light. Even growth is promoted. When the HID is stationary, plants tend to grow toward the lamp. When the lamp is always in the same place, the plants grow up around it, severely shading the rest of the garden. Rotating the plants every few days so they receive more even light distribution solves this problem. It is much easier to move the lamp rather than the plants.

Two: A lamp moving overhead increases the intense light that the majority of plants receive. This is not a substitute for more lumens from an additional lamp. It is a more efficient way to use an HID. Since the lamp will be directly above more plants, they all will receive more direct, intense light. Young clones and seedlings may s-t-r-e-t-c-h, becoming leggy, to get more light if the lamp travels too far away. Start using the light movers after the plants are 12 inches tall and have several sets of leaves.

(3) Light is received by the plants from more directions. Total light energy is optimum for all plants, as long as one plant is not shading another. This promotes even growth.

This drawing simulates the path of the sun over a single plant.

Light Movers

A light mover is a device to move a lamp back and forth across the ceiling of a grow room to provide a more even distribution of light. The methods employed to move the lamp across the ceiling may be motorized or manual, fast moving or moving only once or twice a day. The speed at which the lamp moves is of minimal importance. But the more often it traverses the garden, the more even the profile of the garden will be, and the closer plants can be to the lamp. The unit should not move so fast that the lamp wobbles, making it unstable. It is not necessary for the lamp to move exactly like the sun; whether the lamp moves from east to west is of no consequence. The path it takes should be a consistent, one that distributes light evenly. If the lamp is allowed to stay in the same position for two or three days before it is moved, plants will get uneven light distribution. Motorized units have an advantage in this respect, since they are moving at a constant rate all the time.

These light movers may be purchased from an ever-increasing number of suppliers or constructed by the gardener. There are only two things to be on the lookout for when constructing your own: (1) strength and (2) ease of movement. First and foremost, the rigging overhead must be able to support the weight of the lamp and hood. If the system were to come crashing down on the garden

it could cause a real problem. Besides wrecking your precious garden, it very well could start a fire. Make sure it is secured to the ceiling! The electric cord should not slow down or affect the movement of the light mover in any way. Second, the system should be easy to move. If it is easy to move, chances are that you will move it. Homemade made light movers work best for gardeners who are able to look after their garden two or three times a day, moving the lamp every time.

There are two basic kinds of light movers. The first is a linear system. These systems move in a straight line simulating the sun's path through the heavens. This system increases the intense light to plants in a linear oval. The square footage covered by the system depends on the length of the track and the number of lamps employed. The system uses a track affixed to the ceiling. The lamp moves back and forth across the ceiling, guided by the track. The lamp is hooked to the light mover with an extendible chain or cord so it can be as close as possible to the plants. These units vary as to the length and speed the lamp travels. Some are designed for one lamp, while others are able to move up to six lamps efficiently. A 6-foot linear light mover increases optimum coverage of light from 36 to 72 square feet.

Light Rail II by Gualala Robotics

Three arm Sun Circle

Light Track from Hydrofarm

Two arm Sun Circle with horizontal Hydrofarm reflectors.

Single arm Sun Circle

A homemade alternative to the commercial linear light track is the clothesline unit. It is simple to construct. Eyebolts are attached at opposite ends of the ceiling or ceiling corners. Pulleys are attached to the eyebolts. Between the pulleys, a small diameter, heavy-duty nylon cord is strung in a loop. The HID is attached to the bottom of the loop. This is just like many clotheslines used in tall city buildings that have access from only one end. After the lamp is mounted on the looped cord, it may be moved back and forth as often as desirable - the more often the better. Another variation of the principle stretches a nylon cord across the ceiling. A single pulley is attached to it. Attach the lamp to the pulley, then move the lamp back and forth on the pulley overhead. One industrious person made a light mover out of an old garage door opener. The possibilities are endless. When using these types of units, make sure to watch the profile of the garden. Try to give the garden the most even distribution of light possible.

The second type of light mover is the arc method. It rotates in a pivoting motion. The unit swivels from a boom on a wall or the ceiling overhead. The lamp(s) take an arc-shaped path, covering a little more area than the linear method.

There are two basic types of arc method: (1) wall mount units that swing back and forth in a partial arc on a motorized hinge. (2) ceiling mount units that rotate 360^0 in a circle. The lamp(s) in both types are suspended by an adjustable chainattached to a telescoping boom(s).

Another type of arc method is a homemade model employing 1-inch plumbing pipes. It bolts to the ceiling or is mounted on a wooden frame that is in turn affixed to the ceiling. This unit, like the clothesline unit, is non-motorized. The gardener simply moves the lamp to a different location daily or as often as necessary to maintain an even garden profile.

Commercial glight movers ive more intense light to more plants for less money. Light movers make it possible to use fewer lamps and get the same .yield An increase of 25 to 35 percent in intense light coverage is afforded by light movers. Two lamps mounted on a motorized light mover will do the job of three stationary lamps. Motorized light are preferred because they help maintain an even garden profile. Since the HID is already drawing about 9.2 ,amperes and it is hooked up to a 15- or 20-ampere circuit, it would take a new circuit to hang up another HID. The commercial movers is easily plugged into the same timer and socket as the lamp. Since the motor for the light mover uses about one ampere (75 to 100 watts) of current, it may be attached to the same circuit as the lamp with little risk of overload.

Light movers are normally used for only part of a plant's life. When there are just a few plants, they are huddled directly under the lamp. Using a light mover on too many seedlings or clones causes them to s-t-r-e-t-c-h. One of the good things about homemade units is they do not have a particular cycle they must complete. They are operated by hand and can be placed in any location for as long as desired.

Planter boxes or containerson wheels offer a good alternative to light movers. The containers are rotated daily. The wheels make this job easy. The light reaches every corner of the garden without having to move the lamp. This method has essentially the same effect as moving the lamp overhead, but is more work because all the plants

have to be moved, rather than only one or two lamps.

The 400-watt bulbs offer more even light distribution and the lamp can be closer to the plants since they have less heat buildup than 1000-watt HID's. The 400-watt bulbs offer certain advantages, especially if space is a problem. One gardener uses two of them in a narrow 4-by-8-foot room with amazing success. Another apartment dweller has the brightest closet in town! The 400-watt halides do have a longer life than the 1000-watt lamps, but share the same lumen maintenance curve. For the amount of lumens produced, their initial cost is much higher. However, their life is twice as long - about 20,000 hours. If the 400-watt HID's give you the best value for an even distribution of light, several ballasts may be looped together on the same 220 volt circuit. Ask an electricianfor help. Do not use a 400-watt lamp in a 1000-watt system! It *will* work for the first 24 to 48 hours, then BOOM! The lamp and maybe the ballast will stop working and who-knows-what else!

This small 175-watt metal halide lamp from Hydrofarm will provide enough light for a small garden. It can also be used for side lighting in larger gardens.

Side lighting is another way to provide nearly the same amount of light to the entire garden. Of course this uses more electricity, but it increases the amount of light available to the plants. Probably the most efficient lamp to use in this case is the low-pressure (LP) sodium, since its -lumenpewatt conversion is the highest available. The lamps are mounted where light intensity is marginal, along the walls, to provide side light.

Fluorescent lamps could also be used, but the lumen-per-watt conversion is much lower. Remember the LP sodiums must be used with a halide, which supplies all the blue light the plants need. If you really want to get the most intense light possible in the garden, you may want to employ both side lighting and a light mover.

Cuttings and young seedlings are huddled below the HID when small, and moved into larger containers when they are crowding one another. When they are far enough apart that the light does not afford complete coverage, it is time to use a light mover. Before this time, a light mover might not give them enough intense light and growth might be leggy. However, use a light meter to check to make sure each plant variety gets adequate light.

About Electricity

The basics of electricity really do not need to be understood to grow indoors. Understanding the basics may save you money, time and the shock of your life. First, simple electrical concepts and terms are defined and briefly discussed. Once these terms are understood, you will be able to see the purpose of fuses, wire thickness (gauge), amperes on a circuit, the importance of ground and the necessity to develop safe habits.

Before anything electrical is touched, please remember the rule below.

 RULE OF THUMB: Work backward when installing electrical components or doing wiring. Start at the bulb and work toward the outlet. Always plug in the cord last!

Alternating-Current - an electric current that reverses its direction at regularly occurring intervals.

Ampere (amp) - the measure of electricity in motion. Electricity can be looked at in absolute terms of measurement just as water can. A gallon is an absolute measure of a portion of water; a coulomb is an absolute measure of a portion of electricity. Water in motion is measured in gallons per second and electricity in motion is measured in coulombs per second. When an electrical current flows at one coulomb per second, we say it has one ampere.

Breaker box - an electrical circuit box containing breaker circuit switches.

Breaker switch - an ON/OFF safety switch that will turn the electricity OFF when the circuit is OVERLOADED.

Circuit - the closed path that electricity travels. If this path is interrupted, the power will go off. If this circuit is given a chance, it will travel a circular route through your body! Never give it a chance!

Conductor - something that is able to carry electricity easily. Copper, steel water and the human body are good electrical conductors.

Direct Current - an electrical current that flows only in one direction.

Fuse - an electrical safety device consisting of a fusible metal that MELTS and interrupts the circuit when overloaded. Never replace fuses with pennies or aluminum foil! They will not melt, which interrupts the circuit when overloaded. This is an easy way to start a fire!

Fuse box - an electrical circuit box containing fuses.

> **CAUTION!** The HID lamp operated on an overloaded circuit will blow fuses, switch off breakers and burn wiring. It could wreck the HID system, even start a fire. Pay attention!

CAUTION! Do not handle electricity when you are standing in a puddle of water.

RULE OF THUMB: Use only one 1000-watt HID for each 15 to 20 ampere circuit.

Ground - a means to connect electricity to the ground or earth. Safety is the reason for ground. If a circuit is properly grounded, and the electricity travels somewhere it is not supposed to, it will go via the ground wire into the earth and be rendered harmless. Electricity will travel the path of least resistance. This path must be along the ground wire. It is all right to have several ground wires for extra security.

The ground is formed by a wire (usually green or bare copper) that runs parallel to the circuit and is attached to a metal ground stake. All the circuits in the home are then attached to the ground stake. Metal cold-water pipes serve as excellent conductors for the ground. They are all attached to one another. Water pipes conduct electricity well and are all in good contact with the ground.

The entire system - pipes, copper wire and metal ground stake - conduct any misplaced electricity safely into the ground.

The ground wire is the third wire with the big round prong on a male plug. The ground runs through the ballast all the way to the hood.

HID systems must have a ground that runs a continual path from the socket through the ballast to the main fuse box, then to the house ground. See drawing above.

Hertz - fluctuations or cycles in electricity within a conductor (wire). In the United States, alternating-current electricity runs at 60 HERTZ or cycles per second.

Ohm's Power Law - law that expresses the strength of an electric current: volts x amperes = watts.

Short circuit - side or unintentional circuit formed when conductors (wires) cross. A short circuit will normally blow fuses!

Volts - air, water, gas - virtually anything can be put under pressure. Pressure is measured in pounds per square inch (PSI). Electricity is also under pressure or electrical potential; this pressure is measured in volts. Most home wiring is under the pressure of approximately 110 or 220 volts.

A complete grounded circuit is essential for safety. If you use a ground adaptor, make sure the socket is grounded separately.

Inadequate wire and poor connections almost caused a fire.

Australian indoor gardeners should contact Silverlux, 26 - 30 Northumberland St., (Cnr. of Rokeby St.), Collingwood, Victoria 3066, 613-419-4688 for HID specifications.

Watt - a measure of work. Watts measure the amount of electricity flowing in a wire. When amperes (units of electrons per second) are multiplied by volts (pressure) we get watts. 1000-watts = 1 kilowatt.

A halide lamp that draws about 9.2 amperes X 120 volts = 1104 watts. Remember Ohm's Power Law: amps X watts = volts. This is strange; the answer was supposed to be 1000-watts. What is wrong? The electricity flows through the ballast, which requires energy to run. The energy drawn by the ballast must then amount to 104 watts.

Watt-hours - the amount of watts used in an hour. One watt-hour is equal to one watt used for one hour. A kilowatt-hour is 1000 watt-hours. A 1000-watt HID will use one kilowatt per hour and the ballast will use about one watt. Electrical bills are charged out in kilowatt hours (KWH) (See "Chart on Cost of Electricity", page 44).

Wire and Wiring

Electrical wire comes in all sizes (gauges), and they are indicated by number. The higher the number the smaller the wire; the lower the number the larger the wire (See drawing below). The standard wire in most homes is 14-gauge. Wire size is important for two reasons (1) ampacity (2) voltage drop. Ampacity is the amount of amperes a wire is able to carry safely. Electricity flowing through wire creates heat. The more amps flowing, the more heat created. This heat is wasted power! To avoid this wasted power, the proper thickness of wire must be used: at least 14 gauge. It must be well insulated and must have a ground wire.

● ● ● ● ● •
8 10 12 14 16 18

Wire is rated by number; the smaller the number, the larger the wire.

In addition, forcing too much power (amperes) through a wire also creates voltage drop. Voltage (pressure) is lost in the wire. For example: if you force an 18-gauge wire to carry 9.2 amperes at 120 volts not only would the wire heat up, maybe enough to blow fuses, but the voltage at the outlet would be 120 volts, while the voltage 10 feet away could be as low as 108. Would you like to pay for this unused 12 volts? The farther electricity travels, the more heat is generated and the more voltage drops.

Note: Voltage drop is wasteful, and causes lamps to function very inefficiently. A lamp designed to work at 120 volts that receives only 108 volts (90 percent of the power it was intended to operate at) would produce only 70 percent of the normal light. Use at least 14-gauge wire for any extension cords and if the cord has to carry power over 60 feet, use 12-gauge wire.

A simple electrical circuit requires two wires. One wire runs from the source of power to the load (from the electrical outlet to a ballast for example), and the other wire completes the circuit back to the source of power. There always should be a third or ground wire along with the circuit wires.

Voltage in homes ranges from 110 to 125. Most calculations use 125 volts. The only way to tell the exact voltage available at the outlet is to measure the electricity with a voltmeter.

Wires are usually
Black = hot White or red = common Bare, blue or green = ground

When wiring a plug-in or socket:
The hot wire attaches to the brass or gold screw.
The common wire attaches to the aluminum or silver screw.
The ground wire always attaches to the ground prong.
Take special care to keep the wires from crossing and forming a short circuit.

Outlets and sockets must have a solid connection. If they are jolted around, allowing the electricity to jump, the prongs will burn; a fire could result. Check plug periodically to ensure that they have a solid connection.

If a new circuit or breaker box is necessary, hire an electrician, or purchase *Wiring Simplified*, by H.P. Richter and W.C. Schwan. It costs less than $5. and is available at most hardware stores. Installing a new circuit in a breaker box is very easy, but installing another fuse is more complex. Before trying anything of this scope, read up on it and discuss it with several professionals. You could be in for the shock of your life!

About Electricity Consumption

There are many ways to save energy to compensate for the increase in consumption of electricity. One friend moved into a home that had all electric heat as well as a fireplace. He installed three HID lamps in the basement that generated quite a bit of heat. The excess heat was dispersed by using a vent fan attached to a thermostat/humidistat. He turned off the electric heat, bought a fireplace insert and started heating with wood. Even running three lamps, consuming three kilowatts per hour, the electric bill was less than it had been with electric heat!

A one-to-three-bedroom home can run two or three 1000-watt lamps and a four-or-five-bedroom home can operate three to five lamps with little or no problem. Any more lamps usually require new incoming circuits or the use of present circuits is severely limited. Some friends bought a new, efficient water heater and saved $17 a month! Another indoor gardener set her water heater for 130^0 (55^0 C) instead of 170^0 (76^0 C). This simple procedure saved about 25 kilowatt-hours per month!

Note: Do not turn the water heater any lower than 130^0 F (55^0 C). Harmful bacteria can grow below this safe point!

HID lights are most likely to be used economically where hydroelectric power is plentiful such as the West Coast and the Tennessee-Kentucky area. Some power companies are not able to sell all the power they generate during certain hours of the day. These power companies use coal or nuclear energy to generate electricity. Many of these companies generate electricity during the daylight hours for factories and office buildings, but after 4 or 5 p.m., the power plant will not need to generate electricity; however, it is impractical and uneconomical to shut the plant down. Electrical rates after 4 p.m. are generally greatly discounted. It will probably take quite a bit of power usage to get a good discount, but the rates of some companies are as low as one-third of the cost of prime-time day usage.

Cost of Electricity Chart

Price per killowatt hour	12 hour days		18 hour days	
	day	month	day	month
$.02	.24	7.20	.36	10.80
$.03	.36	10.80	.54	16.20
$.04	.48	14.40	.72	21.60
$.05	.60	18.00	.90	27.00
$.06	.72	21.60	1.08	32.40
$.07	.84	25.20	1.26	37.80
$.08	.96	28.80	1.44	43.20
$.09	1.08	32.40	1.62	48.60
$.10	1.20	36.00	1.80	54.00

Setting Up the HID Lamp

STEP ONE: Before setting up the HID system, read "Setting Up the Grow Room" in Chapter One, pages 11-13, and complete the step-by-step instructions.

STEP TWO: Both the lamp and ballast radiate quite a bit of heat. Care must be taken when positioning them so they are not so close (6 to 12 inches) to plants or flammable walls and ceiling that they become hazardous. If the room is limited in space, with a low ceiling, placing a protective, non-flammable material, such as metal or asbestos, between the lamp and ceiling provides much more space. If the room is 6-by-6-feet or smaller, an

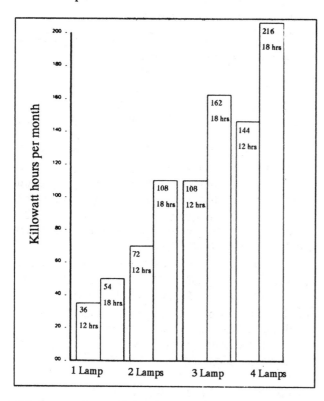

This bar graph compares electric consumption of lamps at 12 and 18 hours of daily use.

exhaust fan will be necessary to keep things cool. It is most effective to place the remote ballast near the floor. It can also be placed outside the grow room if the temperature is too high, which is unlikely when a good vent fan is used. When hanging the lamp on the overhead chain or pulley system, make sure electrical cords are unencumbered and not too close to any heat source.

STEP THREE: Buy a timer! A timer will be necessary for you to play Mother Nature successfully. The reasons for having a timer are obvious. If the HID system is not equipped with a timer, the only way to turn it on and off is to plug and unplug it, a shocking and colorful experience. Mother Nature provides a rigid schedule for plants to count on and live by. When the horticulturist assumes her role, will he or she remember to turn the lamp on and off at exactly the same time each and every day for several months? Or will he or she even be there each and every day, at the same time, twice a day, all year round? (see: photos of various timers.)

This sophisticated timer by Green Air Products offers the an excellent value.

STEP FOUR: To start the HID lamp, it will be necessary to find the proper outlet. A 1000-watt HID lamp uses about 9.5 amperes (amps) of electricity on a regular 110 to 120 volt house current.

A typical home has a fuse box or a breaker box. Each fuse or breaker switch controls an electrical circuit in the home. The fuse or breaker switch will be rated for 15, 20, 25, 30 or 40 amps of service. These circuits are considered overloaded when more than 80 percent of the amps are being used. The fuse will have its amp rating printed on its face, and the breaker switch will have its amp rating printed on the switch. To find out which outlets are controlled by a fuse or breaker switch, remove the fuse or turn the breaker switch off.

This grounded timer is rated at 15 amps and is perfect for one lamp and a light mover.

Test *every* 110-volt outlet in the home to see which ones do not work. All the outlets that do not work are on the same circuit. All outlets that work are on another circuit. When you have found a circuit that has few or no lights, radios, TV's, stereos etc. plugged into it, look at the circuit's amp rating. If it is rated for 15 amps, just plug one 1000-watt HID into it. A leeway of 5.5 amps is there to cover any power surges or incongruities in electricity supply. If the circuit is rated for 20 or more amps, it may be used for the HID lamp as well as a few other low-amp appliances and lights. To find out how many amps are drawn by each appliance, add up the number of watts drawn by each appliance, then divide by 120.

EXAMPLE:

A circuit with a 20-amp fuse containing the following items

1400-watt toaster oven

100-watt incandescent light bulb

20-watt radio

1520 total watts divided by 120 = 12.6 amps in use

The above example shows 12.6 amps are being drawn when everything is on. By adding 9.2 amps, drawn by the HID to the circuit, we get 21.8 amps drawn - AN OVERLOADED CIRCUIT. There are three solutions to this problem: (1) Remove one or all of the high amp consuming appliances and plug them into another circuit. (2) Find another circuit that has few or no amps drawn by other appliances. (3) Install a new circuit. A 220-volt circuit will make more amps available per circuit if using several lamps.

Never replace a smaller fuse with a fuse that has a higher amperage rating. The fuse is the weakest link in the circuit. If a 20-amp fuse is placed into a 15-amp circuit, the fuse is able to conduct more electricity than the wiring. When this happens, the wires burn, rather than the fuse. An overloaded circuit can easily result in a house fire. Please be careful.

CAUTION! An HID lamp operated on and overloaded circuit will blow fuses, switch off breakers or burn wiring. It could wreck the HID system, even start a fire. Pay attention!

 RULE OF THUMB: Use only one 1000-watt HID per 15 to 20 amp (110-volt) circuit. Do not break this rule!

Use an extension cord that is at least 14-gauge wire or heavier if the plug will not reach the outlet desired. The thicker 14-gauge extension cord is more difficult to find and may have to be constructed. A smaller 16- or 18-gauge cord will not conduct adequate electricity and will heat up, straining the entire system. Cut the 14 gauge extension cord to the exact length; the farther electricity travels, the weaker it gets and the more heat it produces, which also strains the system.

STEP FIVE: Always use a 3-prong grounded plug. If your home is not equipped with working 3-prong grounded outlets, buy a 3-prong grounded plug and outlet adaptor. Attach the ground wire to a grounded ferrous metal object, such as a grounded cold-water pipe, or a heavy copper wire

driven into the earth to a form a ground. Screw the ground into the outlet face. You will be working with water under and around the HID system. Water conducts electricity about as well as the human body . . . guaranteed to give you a charge!

STEP SIX: Once the proper circuit is selected, the socket and hood mounted overhead and the ballast in place on the floor (but not plugged in), screw the HID bulb finger-tight into the socket. Make sure the bulb is secured in the socket firmly. The threaded metal base of the bulb should not be seen from under the socket, to make certain there is a good connection. When secure, wipe off all smudges on the bulb to increase brightness.

STEP SEVEN: Plug the three-prong plug into the timer that is in the "off" position. Plug the timer into the grounded outlet, set the timer at the desired photoperiod and turn the timer on. The ballast will hum, the lamp will flicker and slowly warm up, reaching full brilliance in about five minutes.

When installing the bulb, make sure that it is screwed securely into the socket.

STEP EIGHT: When using more than one HID, it is easiest to plug in each lamp individually. This way, flexibility is maintained. If another lamp needs to be hung up or removed, it is easy and does not require more wiring into a central system.

Troubleshooting the HID Lamp

When your light does not shine, your garden does not grow. Finding the reason a HID system does not work is simple and easy when the steps below are followed.

STEP ONE: First, the problem must be isolated. Is the ballast receiving electricity? Plug in the ballast. If it hums, it is receiving electricity. If there is no hum, check the plug and outlet for a firm connection. Check the timer using another light to ensure it functions properly. If there is still no hum, remove the covering over the ballast; check for solid wire connections.

The transformer is the big steel or aluminum box; check it for burns. If you see any burns, take the transformer to a halide dealer for replacement. The starter (HP sodium only) and capacitor look like an oblong tin can. They are burned out if the sealed lip around each end is pinched out or the bottom is bulging (convex). The lip should be completely smooth and unwrinkled. If you can shake the capacitor and hear liquid inside, it is also burned out. When a starter or capacitor is burned out, it must be replaced.

STEP TWO: If the ballast works, the problem must be in the bulb or the wiring between the ballast and the bulb. First check to make sure the bulb is screwed firmly into the socket. *A loose bulb is the most common reason the bulb will not work*. Once the bulb is securely screwed into the socket, check all the connections for heat and firm contact. Always unplug the ballast before touching bare wire or connections. Check the arc tube in bulb for darkness. If the bulb is two to five years old, it could be burned out.

> **CAUTION!** Be extremely careful when handling the capacitor. It can hold an extremely powerful electrical charge for months.

STEP THREE: If a fuse burns out or a breaker switch turns off, there is an overloaded circuit. See information about "Setting Up the HID Lamp" on pages 45-46.

STEP FOUR: If the lamp flickers or pulsates, do not worry. After about 100 hours of operation, the lamp halogens in the arc tube will stabilize and appear to pulsate less. Color changes may also occur. Color changes are normal and will not effect the life or the brilliance of the bulb.

STEP FIVE: HID bulbs become brittle after several hours of use. Handle used bulbs as little as possible to avoid breakage. Wipe finger prints from the bulb after handling to retain full brilliance. When restarting lamp, wait about 15 minutes for the bulb to cool before it will restart.

Chapter Three

Soil and Containers

Flowers and vegetables flourish in rich organic soil as well as soilless mixes. Outdoors, when planted in the earth, roots will branch out and penetrate deep into the soil, in search of water and nutrients. Outdoors, many plants tend to grow above ground at the same rate as they grow below the surface. The roots spread out beyond the drip line. If the root system is inhibited from growing and finding water and nutrients, the entire plant's growth is inhibited. It is important to remember how much root space vegetables and flowers need and provide adequate soil or growing medium to meet those needs. In the indoor environment, roots must be contained in a pot or planter box. It is virtually impossible to provide an indoor soil environment exactly like that found outdoors. This is why extreme care must be taken when selecting soil and containers.

Soil and Amendments

Soil is made up of many mineral particles mixed together with living and dead organic matter that incorporates air and water. Three factors contribute to the root's ability to grow in soil: (1) texture (2) pH and (3) nutrient content.

Texture is governed by the size and physical make up of the mineral particles. The proper soil texture is required for adequate root penetration, water and oxygen retention and drainage, as well as many other complex chemical processes. Clay or adobe soil is made up of very small flat mineral particles. When it gets wet, these minute particles pack tightly together, slowing or stopping root penetration and water drainage.

Roots are unable to breathe because very little or no space is left for oxygen. Water has a very difficult time penetrating these tightly packed soils, and once it does penetrate it, drainage is slow. Sandy soils have much larger particles. They permit good aeration (supply of air or oxygen) and drainage. Frequent watering is necessary, as water retention is very low. The soil's water- and air-holding ability, as well as root penetration, are a function of texture.

Soil texture is easily checked by picking up a handful of moist (not soggy) soil and gently squeezing it. The soil should barely stay together and have sponge-like effect when the hand slowly opens up to release pressure.

Soil amendments increase the soil's air- and water-retaining ability. Soil amendments fall into two categories: mineral and organic.

The amendments in the mineral group are all near neutral on the pH scale and essentially contain no nutrients of their own. Mineral amendments decompose through weathering and erosion, which does not effect soil pH. The amendments are also very lightweight. This is a good point to consider when containers have to be moved often.

Perlite (sand or volcanic glass expanded by heat like popcorn) holds water and nutrients on its many irregular surfaces and works especially well for aerating the soil. This is a good medium for people planning to "push" plants with heavy fertilization. It drains fast and does not promote salt buildup. Perlite is available in three grades: fine, medium and coarse. Medium and coarse are the choice of most gardeners for a soil amendment.

Pumice (volcanic rock) is very light and holds water, nutrients and air, in its many catacomb-like holes. It is a good amendment for aerating the soil and retaining moisture evenly. Pumice is a favorite hydroponic growing medium.

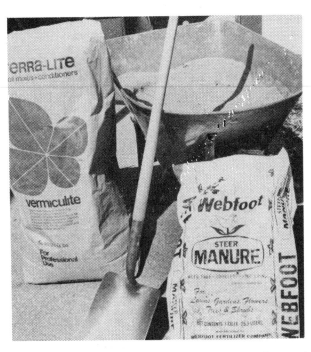

Vermiculite, sand and manure make a popular and inexpensive mix.

Vermiculite (mica processed and expanded by heat) holds water, nutrients and air within its fiber and gives body to fast draining-soils. Fine vermiculite also works very well as a medium in which to root cuttings. This amendment holds more water than perlite or pumice. It works best for water retention in small pots or for people who do not like to water. Vermiculite is used for hydroponic wick systems since it holds so much moisture. Vermiculite comes in three grades: fine, medium and coarse. Always use the fine grade to root cuttings. If fine is not available, crush the coarse or medium grades between your hands, rubbing the palms back and forth. As a soil amendment, coarse vermiculite is the best choice.

Organic soil amendments break down through bacterial activity, slowly yielding humus. Humus is a soft, spongy material that binds minute soil particles together, improving the soil texture. Young, composting, organic soil amendments require nitrogen to carry on their bacterial decomposition. If they do not contain at least 1.5 percent nitrogen, the organic amendments will get it from the soil, robbing roots of nitrogen. When using organic amendments, make sure they are thoroughly composted (at least one year) and releasing nitrogen rather than using it from the soil. A good sign of soil fertility is a dark, rich color.

Some gardeners prefer to use mineral amendments because there is no bacterial activity that alters nutrient content and pH. Others prefer rich, thoroughly composted organic matter that not only amends texture, but supplies available nutrients. Leaf mold, garden compost (at least one year old) and many types of thoroughly composted manure usually contain enough nitrogen for their decomposition needs and are releasing, rather than using, nitrogen. When using organic amendments, it is best to purchase them at a nursery, which helps control quality. Carefully look over the bag to see if it guarantees that it contains no harmful insects, larva eggs, fungus or bad micro-organisms.

Garden compost and leaf mold may be rich and organic, but are usually full of insects and who-knows-what-else. For example, the compost pile is a favorite breeding ground for cutworms. Just one cutworm in a 5-gallon pot means certain death for the defenseless flowers.

Barnyard manure may contain toxic levels of salt and copious quantities of weed seeds and fungus spores. If using manure, purchase it in bags that guarantee its contents or make sure it is well-rotted. There are many kinds of manure: cow manure, horse manure, rabbit manure, chicken manure and the less common pig and duck manure. All of these manures are bulky and can be used as soil amendments. Their nutrient content varies, depending on the diet of the animal and the decomposition factors.

Orchids thrive in mineral amendments like pumice and vermiculite.

Mushroom compost is an excellent organic amendment to soil and soilless mixes. Most growers use about one third mushroom compost with two thirds soil.

Peat is the term used to describe partially decomposed vegetation; the decay has been slowed by the wet and cold conditions of the Northern U.S.

and Canada, where it is found. The most common types of peat are formed from sphagnum and hypnum mosses.

Sphagnum peat moss is light brown, and the most common peat found at commercial nurseries. It retains water well, absorbing 15 to 30 times its own weight. This gives the soil body. It contains essentially no nutrients of its own and the pH ranges from 3 to 5. After decomposing several months, the pH could get *very* acidic. However, fine dolomite lime can be added to compensate and stabilize the pH.

Hypnum peat moss is more decomposed, darker in color, with a higher pH (5 to 7). This peat moss is less common, and contains more nutrients than sphagnum peat moss. This type of peat is a good soil amendment; however, it cannot hold as much water as sphagnum moss.

Peat moss is very dry and difficult to wet the first time, unless you bought it wet, which makes it really heavy. When using peat moss as a soil amendment, it is easiest to dry-mix all of the components, then wet the mix using a wetting agent such as liquid concentrate soap (2 or 3 drops per gallon). Another trick to mixing peat moss is to kick the sack a few times before opening. A few kicks help break up the bail much faster and with less mess.

pH and Lime

PH is a scale from 1 to 14 that measures acid-to-alkaline balance. 1 is the most acidic, 7 is neutral, and 14 is most alkaline. Most plants will grow best in soil with a pH from 6 to 7. Within this range, most vegetables and flowers can properly absorb and process available nutrients. If the pH is too low (acidic), the nutrients are chemically bound by acid salts and the roots are unable to absorb them. An alkaline soil, with a high pH, will cause toxic salt buildup and limit water intake by roots. Hydroponic solutions perform best in a pH range a little lower than for soil. The pH range that is for hydroponics is from 5.5 to 6.8, 6.0 being ideal for most plants.

There are several ways to measure pH. A pH soil test kit, litmus paper, or an electronic pH tester may be found at most nurseries. When testing pH, take two or three samples and follow the directions for the soil test kit, litmus paper or electronic pH tester to the letter. There are several brands of soil test kits on the market. They cost $10 to $30 and will measure soil pH and N-P-K content by mixing soil with a chemical solution. Make sure you buy a kit with a set of directions that you understand.

This digital pH meter helps keep the pH in the "safe" range.

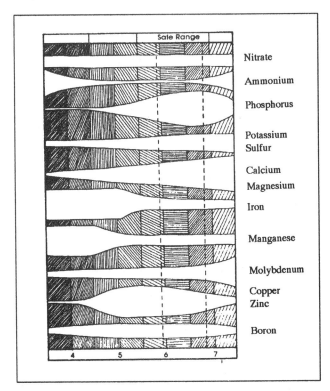

The nutrients listed in this chart are most readily available in the safe pH of 5.9 to 6.8.

If using litmus paper, collect soil samples that demonstrate an average of the soil. Place the samples in a clean jar and moisten with distilled water. Place two pieces of the litmus paper in the muddy water. After 10 seconds, remove one of the pieces. Wait a minute and remove the other one. Both pieces of litmus paper should be the same color. The litmus paper container should have a pH color chart on the side; match the color of the litmus paper with the colors on the chart to get a pH reading. The only way litmus paper could give a false reading is if the fertilizer (Peters, Ra-Pid-Gro, Miracle-Gro etc.) contains a color tracing agent or the pH of the distilled water used for the test was not a neutral 7.

There are many brands of electronic soil pH testers. They are inexpensive ($15 to $30), very convenient and fairly accurate. Pay special attention to the soil moisture. Most electronic testers are designed to work in soil that is very moist. When checking pH regularly, the electronic tester is much more economical than test kits and more convenient than litmus paper. The electronic unit will test pH an infinite number of times, while the small chemical test kits are good for only about a dozen tests. For an accurate test, clean the probes of the pH meter after each test with an abrasive agent that wipes clean any corrosion; pack the soil tightly around the probes; water soil with distilled or neutral pH water before testing.

Check the pH of the water being used. Sometimes the pH of the water is too low or too high. After repeated watering, an unacceptable pH can substantially alter the pH of the soil, especially with soils high in organic amendments. Coastal, rainy climates generally have acidic water, while desert regions are prone to alkaline water. A pH problem may surface in the late autumn, when all the leaves fall and vegetation is decomposing. This biodegradation process is acidic by nature and may create an artificially low pH. The acidic leaves lower the pH of the outside soil, and in turn lower the pH of the ground water. This problem is most common among smaller municipal and well-water systems. Generally, larger water facilities carefully monitor and correct pH so there are fewer problems for the gardener. Be on the lookout for any major environmental changes that could affect the water pH. It is very important to keep an eye on the pH at all times.

RULE OF THUMB: Check pH at least once every two weeks.

Soil pH should be between 6 and 7 for maximum growth and nutrient uptake in most plants.

Commercial potting soil almost never has a pH over 7.5. A lower pH is more usual - even as low as 5.5. The ideal range would be between 6 and 6.5. Most potting soils have a tendency to be a bit acidic since they are generally used for indoor, perennial, acid-loving plants. The easiest way to maintain and raise the pH is to mix in one cup of fine dolomite lime per cubic foot of potting soil. Mix dolomite lime thoroughly into dry soil. Mix the soil again in the container after it has been watered. This ensures a thorough, even mix.

Fine dolomite lime has been a favorite pH stabilizer of gardeners for many years. It is virtually impossible to apply too much dolomite as long as it is thoroughly mixed. It stabilizes the pH safely. That is, by adding dolomite to the soil when planting, the pH is guaranteed to remain stable, even with changes in the water supply and acidic fertilizers. Dolomite lime is a compound of magnesium and calcium, which accounts for its immense popularity among gardeners. Both of these secondary nutrients are needed by flowers and vegetables to flower and fruit. Many fertilizers do not supply adequate amounts of calcium and magnesium. Dolomite does not save the soil from excess salt buildup; only you, Mother Nature, and regular leaching will take care of toxic salts. When purchasing dolomite, ask for the finest (dust-like) grade available. Since it will be used for only a few months, the dolomite should be as fine as possible so it is readily assimilable. Coarse dolomite could take as long as a year before it starts to break down enough for the plants to assimilate.

Make sure to mix fine dolomite thoroughly with the soil when planting. Improperly mixed, the dolomite will form a cake or layer that burns roots and deflects water.

 RULE OF THUMB: When planting, add one cup of fine dolomite lime to each cubic foot (or one ounce per gallon) of planting medium to stabilize the pH and provide calcium and magnesium.

Hydrated lime is very similar to dolomite lime, but as the name hydrated implies, it is very soluble. Hydrated lime works acceptably to alter pH *after* planting. Mix it thoroughly with warm water and apply with each watering. Many horticulturists use a mix of one fourth hydrated lime and three fourths dolomite lime. This mix provides lime that is immediately available to neutralize the pH; the dolomite lime has a long-lasting effect. It is not advisable to use more than one cup of hydrated lime per cubic foot of soil. With only hydrated lime in a

soil mix, it is released so fast that it can become toxic to plants. But it is washed out within a couple of weeks.

Small tomato seedlings are emerging from Jiffy-7 pellets.

Whitewash is made from hydrated lime and table salt. The recipe is printed on sacks of hydrated lime. Whitewash is not as viscous as latex paint, and requires a few coats. I really like whitewash because it sticks to damp concrete basement walls and is antiseptic against fungus. Whitewashing is the most effective way to safely "white out" damp, sweaty walls. The famous Bordeaux fungicide mix uses hydrated lime and copper sulfate. Hydrated lime may also be used as a grow room fungicide. Just sprinkle it on the floor and around the room. It will kill fungus on contact.

Use quicklime only in small doses; it can be toxic to plants. Calcic lime contains only calcium and is not a good choice for plant growth. It does not have the buffering qualities of dolomite, nor does it contain any magnesium.

There are several ways to raise the pH. Each requires putting some form of alkali in the growing medium or water, such as calcium carbonate, potassium hydroxide, sodium hydroxide or several other compounds. Both hydroxides are caustic and require special care when handling. They are normally used to raise the pH of hydroponic nutrient solutions. The easiest and most convenient way to raise the pH and stabilize it is to add fine dolomite lime and hydrated lime before planting.

 RULE OF THUMB: To raise the pH one point, add three cups of fine dolomite lime to one cubic foot of soil. An alternate fast-acting mix would be 2 1/2 cups of dolomite and half cup of hydrated lime to one cubic foot of soil.

Types of Lime

Agricultural or ground limestone (calcium carbonate) is one of the most common forms of lime and an excellent choice. It is slow acting and will remain in the soil for several years.

Dolomite lime (calcium magnesium carbonate) combines calcium with magnesium to formulate an excellent pH-altering substance and adds two much used nutrients as well. Always buy slow-acting dolomite in the finest form available so it becomes available sooner. Even the finest grade will remain in the soil for up to five years.

Ground oyster shells contain calcium carbonate and small amounts of phosphorus. These shells are commonly available at feed stores. They are used as chicken grit to supply calcium. Oyster shells are very slow acting, regulating the pH for years.

Hydrated lime (calcium hydroxide) is quick acting and caustic to plants and microorganisms. Use only in small amounts if used at all.

Quicklime (calcium oxide), manufactured by searing or burning limestone, is fast acting, but caustic and may burn or kill plant and soil microorganisms.

Wood ashes are a source of lime as well as potassium (potash) and many ashes contain magnesium. Hardwood ashes are about twice as alkaline as softwood ashes. The main drawback to wood ashes is that they leach out of the soil rapidly.

There are many ways to lower the pH. If the water has a pH that is slightly high, distilled white vinegar will solve the problem. Calcium nitrate or nitric acid, used mainly in hydroponic systems, and sulfur also work very well to lower pH. If using fertilizers containing these nutrients, keep close watch on the pH; they could lower it substantially.

 RULE OF THUMB: To lower the pH of water one point, add one teaspoon of white distilled vinegar per gallon of water. Check pH of the solution before watering because the pH of vinegar varies according to type and manufacturer.

If uncertain how much solution to apply to alter the pH, give a dosage of half as much as recommended, then check it. Wait about 15 minutes and check it again. Now add the balance

of the chemical or as much as needed to achieve the desired result.

After altering the pH, check it, then check it again several days later. Continue checking the pH weekly to make sure it remains stable.

 RULE OF THUMB: If soil pH is under 5 or over 8, it is easiest, and less expensive in the long run, to change soil rather than experimenting with changing the pH.

Pulverized eggshells, clam or oyster shells and wood ashes have a high pH and will raise pH. It takes many, many eggshells to fill a cup and it takes a long time for the shells to break down to affect the pH; wood ashes usually have a pH of about 11 and are easy to over-apply, since they are soluble. Many times ashes come from fireplaces or wood stoves that have been burning all kinds of (plastic and colored inks) trash and are therefore unsafe. Do not use contaminated wood ashes!

Potting soil, fresh out of the bag, generally supplies rapid-growing annuals with enough nutrients for the first month of growth, before supplemental fertilization is necessary. Secondary and trace elements are usually found in sufficient quantities and unnecessary to add, except for fine dolomite lime. If you grow organically, supplemental fertilization can be replaced by organic soil amendments and fertilizers. See Chapter Four, "Organic Fertilizers" pages 66-68.

Potting soil from a nursery is the easiest soil to use for indoor cultivation. It is usually pH balanced, contains adequate levels of most nutrients, retains water and air evenly, drains well, and allows easy root growth. Most potting soils, except those containing unusually large amounts of organic fertilizer amendments, will be depleted of nutrients within three or four weeks. After this time, supplemental fertilization will usually be necessary. Potting soils tend to be very localized, since they are so heavy and shipping costs prohibitive. There are many good brands to choose from. Ask your nurseryperson for help in selecting one. None-the-less, make a point of checking the pH yourself.

Mushroom compost is an inexpensive potting soil amendment. Frequently mushroom compost has been sterilized chemically so that only mushrooms would grow in it. The law usually requires that after mushroom gardeners discard the rich compost, and that it sit fallow for a year or more before it is can be used. The fallow time allows for all the harmful sterilants to leach out. The compost is very fertile since it has been allowed to decompose for many years. Check at your local nursery or extension service for a good source of mushroom compost. Some of the most abundant vegetable harvests use mushroom compost as the main growing medium.

Potting soils containing more than 50 percent vermiculite, pumice or perlite may tend to stratify when heavily saturated with water before planting. The light mineral amendments tend to float, with the heavier organic matter settling to the bottom. If this happens, mix the water-saturated soil thoroughly with your hands until it is evenly mixed before planting or transplanting.

Soil Temperature

Raising the soil temperature speeds chemical processes faster and hastens nutrient uptake. Ideally, the soil temperature should range from 65 to 75^0 F (18 to 24^0 C). The soil can be heated by means of heat cable placed in or under soil. Heat cable may be purchased at most nurseries. Some gardeners use a waterbed heating pad to heat a large bed. It is an inexpensive alternative to heating the air. Soil can be heated passively by placing the container up off the floor on blocks to allow the flow of warm air underneath. Using this method, an additional heat source may not be needed. Do not heat the soil or nutrient solution over 75^0 F (24^0 C). It will dehydrate and cook the roots!

Potting soil can get somewhat expensive when used only once, then discarded. If it is used for more than one crop for several years, undesirable micro-organisms and insects may have time to get started. Nutrients are depleted, water and air retention are poor and compaction leads to poor, drainage. There is an inexpensive alternative to potting soil: soilless mix.

Soilless Mix

Soilless mix is a very popular, inexpensive, lightweight sterile growing medium that has been used in nurseries for many years. It is generally made from one or all of the following: pumice, vermiculite, perlite, sand and peat moss. Soilless mix is a favorite of many. It allows for good, even root growth. It can be pushed to amazing lengths with total control; and best of all, it is very inexpensive!

Soilless mix is preferred by commercial nurserypeople and indoor gardeners alike. It has good texture. It contains essentially no nutrients of its own, unless fortified with nutrients, and is generally at or near 7 on the pH scale. Soilless mix works very well for gardeners who tend to over-water, or over-fertilize, or like to "push" plants with heavy fertilization. It drains fairly rapidly and may be leached efficiently to stop nutrients from building up to toxic levels. Soilless mix can be purchased ready-mixed in bags of Jiffy Mix, Ortho Mix or Terra-lite. Some gardeners say these mixes hold moisture too long and they add 10 to 50 percent perlite to help drainage. These commercial soilless mixes are fortified with small amounts of all necessary nutrients. The fortified nutrients generally last for about a month. None-the-less, it is a good idea to use a fertilizer containing trace elements. After one month, supplemental fertilization can be necessary to sustain vigorous growth in annuals.

Soilless components can be purchased separately and mixed to the desired consistency. Mix small amounts right in the bag. Larger batches should be mixed in a wheelbarrow or on a concrete slab.

Note: Mixing soil or soilless mix is a dusty, messy, miserable job; mix it outdoors and wear a respirator. A light misting of water will help quell dust.

 RULE OF THUMB: Mix soilless amendments outdoors and when they are dry. Use a respirator to avoid dust inhalation.

Coarse sand, fine vermiculite or perlite works well for rooting cuttings. Sand and perlite are fast draining, which helps prevent damping-off. Vermiculite holds water and air longer and makes cloning easier. Soilless mix also allows for complete control of critical nutrient and root-stimulating hormone additives, essential to asexual propagation.

Texture of soilless mix should be coarse, light and spongy. This allows drainage, with sufficient moisture and air retention, as well as providing good root penetration qualities. Fine soilless mix holds more moisture and works well with smaller containers. Soilless mixes using more perlite and sand drain faster, making it easier to push with fertilizer and not lead to excessive salt buildup. Vermiculite and mosses hold water longer and are great for small pots, rooting cuttings or situations that require good water retention.

PH is generally a neutral 7. If using more than 15 percent moss in your mix, add the appropriate amount of dolomite or hydrated lime to correct and stabilize pH. Check the pH every week or two; continued watering can promote a lower pH. Soilless mix tends to maintain a neutral pH easily; it is mainly composed of mineral particles that are not affected by organic decomposition, which could change pH. The pH is affected very little by acidic fertilizers or by water with a high or low pH.

Nutrients are not contained in soilless mix unless they are fortified or added by the gardener. Feed frequently with a soluble complete N-P-K fertilizer containing all necessary trace and secondary elements.

Here are a few examples of the many soilless mixes:

1/3 peat moss
1/3 perlite
1/3 vermiculite

1/8 peat moss
1/8 coarse sand
1/4 vermiculite
1/2 perlite

1/8 peat moss
1/8 coarse sand
1/4 perlite
1/2 vermiculite

1/2 peat moss
1/2 perlite

Add the proper amount of dolomite or hydrated lime to each mix to bring pH up to neutral. See **RULE OF THUMB** page 52.

Note: When using sand to root cuttings or as an additive to soil or soilless mix, make sure it is washed, coarse sand; it will drain much better than fine sand. Do not use beach or ocean sand; it contains toxic levels of salt. Sand is the heaviest soil amendment; if too much is used, it will settle to the bottom, while the perlite and vermiculite remain on top.

Rockwool root cubes or Jiffy 7 Pellets and Oasis cubes are the neatest invention since the crutch. These root cubes and peat pots are very convenient and lend themselves to growing cuttings or seedlings with a strong root system. Peat pots are small compressed peat moss containers with an expandable outside wall. The flat pellets pop up into a seedling pot when watered. They work very well for sowing seeds or even rooting cuttings. Just place the seed or cutting in the wet peat pot or root cube and keep it evenly moist. For cuttings, make sure to crimp the top in around the stem so constant contact is made between the stem and the root cube or peat pot. When roots show through the side, set pot or cube into a larger pot. There will be virtually no transplant shock. They do tend to dry out and contract, which exposes stems. Be sure to check peat pots or root cubes daily, keeping them evenly moist but not drenched. Root cubes and peat pots do not contain any nutrients. Seedlings do not require any nutrients for the first week. Feed seedlings after the first week and cuttings as soon as they are rooted. One gardener likes to feed cuttings and seedlings a weak manure tea when they are planted and with each watering for the first two weeks.

Soil Mixes

Some gardeners like to mix their own soil. Many of them go out to the back yard and dig up some good-looking dirt that drains poorly, and retains water and air unevenly. This dirt is then mixed with garden compost, full of micro-organisms and bugs. They think this unique soil mix will grow the best produce possible and besides, it is much cheaper than buying it! The truth of the matter is that by saving 10 on soil, they will pay for it many times over in fruit and flowers that were not produced. If you choose to mix your own soil, buy all of the components at the nursery. Alternatives that require more work are to sterilize amendments by baking in the oven at 160^0 F (71^0 C) for 30 to 45 minutes. The stench is horrible (you are cooking bugs), not to mention the mess. Or cooking the compost in a pile that reaches 160^0 F (71^0 C). This bakes all the bad insects and diseases, but leaves. If using garden soil, be sure to find the richest, darkest soil with a good texture. From 30 to 70 percent perlite, vermiculite, and peat will probably be necessary as soil amendments. Even well-draining garden soils tend to compact and need more fluff for good drainage, water and air retention. Check the pH before digging soil to make sure it is within the acceptable 6 to 7 range. Add fine dolomite regardless of the pH. Check it two or three times after mixing to ensure that the pH has stabilized.

Compost

Many gardeners have no trouble using organic compost. Others lose their entire garden or have poor yields due to disease in the compost. Many good compost recipes are available from monthly publications such as *Sunset, Organic Gardening, Mother Earth News Magazines* or from the companies specializing in organic composts.

A good compost pile would have cow manure - the older the better - or any kind of manure that is handy. (See Box below). Manure from horse stalls or feed lots is mixed with straw or bedding. Make sure the bedding is not sawdust. Sawdust is very acidic and will leach all of the nitrogen out of the pile as well. The best kind of manure to acquire is the oldest, rottenest possible. It is less prone to have any weed seeds that are still alive. Fresh grass clippings are one of my favorites to use in a compost pile. The clippings are full of nitrogen, which speeds decomposition. Put your hand down deep into a pile of grass clippings that has been in the sun for a couple of hours . . . Now, that's hot!

Horse and sheep manures are *hot* because they contain little water and lots of air. They heat up readily in a compost pile. Cow and pig manures are *cold* because they hold a lot of water and can be compacted easily, squeezing out the air. Worm castings and bat guano are considered *sweet* because their nutrients are immediately available to plants and they will not burn. Most city zoos offer the manure and bedding from the animals at the zoo. This Zoo Doo, as it is called in Portland, is full of nutrients, and weed seeds, It should be composted for at least a year before it is used indoors.

The best way to build a compost pile is high, and keep turning it. Good compost pile recipes include the addition of organic trace elements, enzymes and the primary nutrients. Retail nurseries generally sell compost starter with all the necessary ingredients for a healthy compost pile. The organic matter used should be ground up and in the form of shredded leaves and grass. Do not use large woody branches that could take years to decompose.

This compost pile is covered with black plastic visqueen.

Before using compost, pour it through 14-inch-mesh hardware cloth (screen). Place a heavy duty framed screen over a large garbage can or a wheelbarrow to catch the sifted compost. This will break up the humus before it is mixed with the soil and amendments. After adding the amendments, the mix may be resifted for additional mixing. Earthworms found on the screen should be returned to the medium. Cutworms are promptly squished.

Gardeners using one-third worm castings one-third perlite and one-third organic matter have had excellent results. Many gardeners mix a third to half perlite with a bag of rich potting soil that has lots of worm castings. Worm castings are heavy, compacting the roots, and leave little or no air space to the roots. Adding perlite aerates the soil.

Here are three basic examples of the many possible combinations of soil mixes.

Add fine dolomite lime to each one of these soil mixes, whether or not the pH is off. See RULE OF THUMB, page 52.

1/3 worm castings
1/3 manure
1/3 coarse sand

1/3 worm castings
1/3 peat moss
1/3 compost

1/3 peat moss
1/3 perlite
1/3 worm castings

Containers

Containers come in all shapes and sizes. They can be constructed of almost anything; clay, metal, plastic, wood and fiber are the most common. Just about any kind of container will do, as long as it is large enough, thoroughly clean and has not been used for any petroleum or other toxic products. See the chart on "Minimum Container Size" page 58. Clay, fiber and wood containers breathe better than plastic or metal. Clay pots are heavy and notorious for absorbing moisture from soil inside, causing the soil inside to dry out quickly.

Grow bags are a good, inexpensive, long-lasting alternative to rigid containers. In fact, some people use the sack the potting soil came in as a container. Once the soil is inside and moist, the bag holds its shape. The bags tend to expand and contract with the soil, lessening the chance of burned root tips that grow down the side of pots.

Fiber or pulp pots are very popular and inexpensive, but their bottoms frequently rot out. Painting the inside of the fiber container with latex paint will extend the life.

This lime tree needs to be flushed with water. Note the cut in photo on the left that shows the excess salt build-up on the side of the pot.

Automatic self-watering pots are used for African violets and most other gesneriads. These kind of pots work very well for slower-growing perennials. One end of a wick made from coarse string or yarn soaks in water; the other end is packed into the soil. The porous yarn or string wicks water to the soil.

Other than making sure containers are clean, there are two important factors to consider: drainage holes and size.

Drainage holes should let the excess water drain easily, but not be so big that soil in the bottom of the container washes out onto the floor. Pots can be lined with newspaper if drainage is too rapid or soil washes out drain holes. Covering holes will slow drainage, so be wary!

 RULE OF THUMB: Have at least two half-inch or four quarter-inch holes per square foot of container bottom. When using a tray under the pot, do not let excess water sit in the tray longer than three days. This stagnant water causes root rot and fungus.

The size of container is of utmost importance. Most flowers and vegetables are annual plants that grow very rapidly, requiring a lot of root space for vigorous growth. If the roots are confined, growth slows to a crawl. A good example is found at most retail nurseries about midsummer. Tomato plants that are still in small 4-inch or gallon pots that will be fully mature and have a few ripe tomatoes. Notice the branches do not extend much beyond the sides of the container and dripline; the plants are tall and leggy with curled-down leaves. They have an overall stunted sickly appearance. These plants are pot- or root-bound. Sure, they could be kept alive or maybe even forced to grow a little by fertilizing with the exact balance of necessary nutrients. This is a lot of work, it is easy to over-fertilize, and the plant will always be a runt.

Annual plant roots develop and elongate quickly, growing down and out, away from the main taproot. When roots reach the sides of the pot, they grow straight down. Soil contracts and separates from the inside of the container's wall. The root hairs along this gap are responsible for absorbing water and nutrients. They are left helpless to dry out and die. One way to help solve this contraction problem is to run your finger around the inside lip of the pot, cultivating the soil, filling the crack between the pot and soil. Check this gap every few days. Also, maintaining evenly moist soil will help keep root hairs on the soil perimeter from drying out.

A bright halide and coarse, fast-draining soil help create a perfect natural environment for this crop of cacti.

It is important to transplant before the plant is pot-bound and stunted. Once a plant is stunted, it will take several weeks to grow enough new roots and root hairs to resume normal growth.

MINIMUM CONTAINER SIZE	
AGE/MONTHS	CONTAINER SIZE
0-1	4-inch
1-2	1 gallon
2-3	2 gallon
3-4	3 gallon
4-5	5 gallon
4-6	10 gallon

This chart shows the approximate size container for peppers at various ages.

The best way to solve the pot-bound problem is to plant annual seedlings or cuttings directly into a five or six gallon pot. This method requires fewer containers and less work. It is less stressful to both plants and transplanter.

RULE OF THUMB: Allow one gallon of soil for every month the annual will spend in the container. A three-to-six-gallon pot will support a seedling or cutting for three to six months.

Pots are the most common containers for indoor use. They are inexpensive and readily available. Complete individual water and nutrient control is possible with pots. An individual plant can be quarantined from the rest of the garden or dipped in a medicinal solution. When plants are small, they can be huddled tightly together under the HID lamp and moved farther apart as needed.

A drip watering system makes irrigation easy. These systems use low-pressure plastic pipe with friction fittings. Water flows down the pipe and out the emitters, one drop at a time. The emitters are attached to the main hose and are either spaghetti or nipple type. There are several kits on the market, or you can construct your own system from component parts.

The drip system offers several advantages. Once set up, it cuts watering maintenance. Fertilizer can also be injected into the system. Fertilization is easy, but the same amount of nutrient to each plant on the water line. One gardener loves the convenience and constant feeding ability of the system. She injects a fertilizer solution into the system with each watering. She notes that plants grown using a drip system are able to survive in smaller containers. Root growth is minimal, since the nutrients and water are in constant supply. In fact, a soilless mix and a drip system is essentially a non-recovery hydroponic system.

The drip system can also be attached to a timer so that it irrigates when you, Mother Nature, are on vacation. This is very convenient, but can be expensive, not only in monetary terms but in yield as well. The automated system can promote negligence. The garden needs daily care! If it is automated, it may discourage you from actually checking the moisture with a meter or looking at every plant daily. Automation is great, but is not a substitute for good gardening practices.

Large planters can be placed on the ground or set up on blocks or casters to allow air circulation underneath. Increased circulation lessens the chance of fungus growth and keeps the soil warmer than if it were sitting on a cold floor. The planters range in size from 2 feet by 2 feet by 12 inches to 10 feet by 10 feet by 24 inches. The roots have 2 to 3 times as much soil to grow in and much less side surface for roots to run into and grow down. Roots are able to intertwine and grow to their potential.

Large planters on casters are easy to maneuver in the grow room and provide more root space for plants.

Generally plants or cuttings are left in one-gallon pots until they are a month to six weeks old, then transplanted to the large planter box before they are root-bound. This allows young plants to be bunched together under the lamp and receive maximum light intensity. As many as 20 plants can be placed in a 2 feet by 2 feet by 12 inch planter, but 4 to 6 plants are much more reasonable. Once plants start crowding and shading one another, they can be bent outward and tied down to a trellis that is nailed to the sides of the planter. Large planters work very well and are highly recommended because they require less maintenance. Since there is a larger mass of soil, water and nutrients are retained much longer and more evenly.

Raised beds can be installed right on the earthen floor of a garage or basement. If drainage is poor, a layer of gravel or a dry well is laid under 12 to 24 inches of soil, with a 2-by-12-inch board border for the raised bed. If the bed is subterranean, it might be very close to the water table. When it rains, the water collects underneath, and might flood the garden. The garden seldom needs watering, but plants are kept a little too wet and there might be a buildup of salts (nutrients) in the soil, since it cannot be leached effectively.

If drainage does not present a problem, and you are able to grow in a raised bed, by all means do so. The large soil mass gives a chance to build up a good organic base after several crops. There will need to be organic activity within the soil. Your job is to make sure it is the good, not the bad, micro-organisms that live in the bed. When mixing soil or adding amendments, use the best possible organic components and follow organic principles. There should be good drainage and the soil should be as deep (12 to 24 inches) as possible. The more organic matter present, the more fertile the soil will be.

A good deal of heat can be generated by the organic activity. This not only speeds nutrient uptake, but helps heat the room as well. Ventilation is necessary to lower heat and humidity. It also keeps the room free of fungus and bad bugs. The organic garden may sound great, but replicating the great outdoors can be a lot of work. Another drawback to the raised bed is that the crop will take a few days to a couple of weeks longer to mature than if it were grown in containers. However, this longer wait is offset by a larger harvest. When plants are grown in a container, with roots restricted from growing, they generally mature and flower faster.

Sowing Seeds Step-by-Step

In this example we will use a one-gallon plastic pot, which is readily available and reusable.

STEP ONE: Acquire the desired number of clean pots.

STEP TWO: Fill each pot with well-mixed growing medium to about an inch from the top.

STEP THREE: Water with one to two quarts of warm water or until the soil is completely saturated and excess water runs out the drain holes. Wait 15 minutes and repeat watering to ensure saturation of the soil.

STEP FOUR: With your finger, make one to 10 small holes one-forth to one-half-inch deep in the surface. Place one to three seeds per hole and cover with soil. Pack it down gently, but firmly in place. Place a paper towel over the seeds to keep seeds surface moist.

STEP FIVE: Sprinkle water on the surface. Make sure seeds remain at proper depth and do not wash out.

STEP SIX: Keep the soil surface evenly moist until seeds sprout. Remove the paper towel as soon as the first seed sprouts.

STEP SEVEN Thin to one plant per pot.

Chapter Four

Water and Fertilizer

Water and fertilizer work hand in hand. The nutrients in fertilizer dissolve in water. Water carries nutrients through the plant. Water is essential to plant growth, making up more than 75 percent of a plant's weight.

The root hairs absorb water, nutrients (fertilizer) and oxygen in the soil and carry them up the stem to the leaves. This flow of water from the soil through the plant is called the transpiration stream. A fraction of the water is processed and used in photosynthesis. The water evaporates into the air, carrying waste products along with it, via the stomata in the leaves. This process is called transpiration. Some of the water also returns manufactured sugars and starches to the roots.

Unfortunately, common tap water may contain high levels of alkaline salts, sulfur or chlorine, and may have a pH out of the acceptable 6 to 7 range. Water containing sulfur is easily smelled and tasted. Saline water is a little more difficult to detect. Water in coastal areas is generally full of salt, because it washes inland from the ocean. This problem is worst in Southern California and other coastal areas.

Chlorine and salt are added to many household water systems. Chlorine, in small doses, does not seem to affect plant growth, but salt-softened water should be avoided. Enough salt will kill any plant! Chlorine does tend to make soil acidic after repeated use.

The best way to get chlorine out of water is to let it sit one or two days in an open container. The chlorine will evaporate as a gas when it comes in contact with the air. An aquarium heater is excellent for heating the water of a reservoir to maintain it at room temperature. Heating also makes the chlorine dissipate faster. If chlorine alters soil pH noticeably, it can be adjusted with hydrated lime. Salts from saline water or fertilizer residue can build up to toxic levels quickly in container gardens. Excessive salts inhibit seed germination, burn root hairs and the tips and edges of leaves. Excess salt built up in the soil can easily be leached out by pouring two gallons of water per gallon of growing medium. Repeat leaching once or twice if burn is severe. Leaching will wash out any toxic buildup of salts. If you use soft or saline water, or have any unwanted substances in the soil, to leach containers every month or two. Hard or well water may be alkaline and usually contains notable amounts of calcium and magnesium. Both micronutrients are put to good use by flowering and fruiting plants. It is doubtful that hard water could contain enough calcium or magnesium to toxify the soil. It is still a good idea to leach the soil at least every two months. Generally, water that is OK to drink is OK for plants.

Watering

There is no wet and dry rule about how much water to apply or when to apply it.

RULES OF THUMB: Apply tepid (70 to 80⁰ F, 22 to 27⁰ C) water. Plants are able to process tepid or room-temperature water rapidly and it penetrates the soil better. Tepid water does not shock tender root hairs or leaves. Would you rather jump into a warm or a cold swimming pool? What happens to your body when you dive into a cold swimming pool?

Water early in the day so excess water will evaporate from soil surface and leaves. Keeping foliage and soil wet leads to fungus attack.

Large plants use much more water than small plants, but there are many more variables than size that dictate a plant's water consumption. The age of the plant, container size, soil texture, temperature, humidity and ventilation all contribute to water needs. Change any one of these variables and water consumption will change. Good ventilation is essential to promote transpiration, water consumption and rapid growth. The healthier a plant, the faster it grows and the more water it consumes.

These geraniums use as much water under a HID as they would under natural sunlight in the middle of a hot summer day.

Many gardeners irrigate on a wet and dry cycle. They water,   then let the soil dry out to about 2 inches below   the soil surface before the next watering. Other gardeners keep moisture more consistent by irrigating more often. A fertilizer solution is often added with each watering.

Annual   flowers and vegetables do not like soggy soil. Soil kept too wet drowns roots, making it impossible for them to breathe. Slow growth and possible fungus attack result. Tiny root hairs dry up and die if the soil dries out, even in pockets. It seems to take forever for the roots to grow new hairs.

A moisture meter takes most of the guesswork out of watering. They can be purchased for $10 to $30 and are well worth the money. The meter can tell exactly how much water the soil contains at any level or point. Many times, soil develops dry pockets and loses its ability to hold water evenly. Checking moisture with a finger is, at best, an educated guess and disturbs the root system. A moisture meter gives an exact moisture reading without bothering the roots as much.

RULES   OF   THUMB: Irrigate   small seedlings and cuttings when the soil surface is dry. For cuttings rooting in sand or vermiculite with good drainage and no humidity tent, the surface is dry almost daily.

Irrigate larger plants in the vegetative and flowering stages when soil is dry 2 inches below the surface. Contrary to popular belief, flowering plants use high levels of water to carry on rapid floral formation. Letting a flowering plant wilt between watering actually stunts flower formation.

Line pots up so it is easy to keep track of the ones that have been watered.

The trick is to apply enough water so that all of the soil gets wet and not let too much run out the drain holes. A leaching effect that carries away nutrients is caused by excessive watering. None-the-less, a little drip (about 10 percent) out the drain holes is beneficial.

Over-watering is a common problem, especially with small plants. Too much water drowns roots by cutting off their supply of oxygen. If you have symptoms of over-watering, buy a moisture meter! It will let both you and your garden breathe easier. Sometimes, parts of the soil are over-watered and other soil pockets remain bone-dry. Cultivating the soil surface, allowing even water penetration, and using a moisture meter will overcome this problem.

A water meter makes watering very exact.

One of the main causes of over-watering is poor ventilation. The plant needs to transpire and water needs to evaporate into the air. If there is nowhere for this wet, humid air to go, gallons of water are locked in the grow room to literally hang in the air. Good ventilation carries the wet air away, replacing it with new dry air. If using trays to catch runoff water, use a turkey baster (large syringe) or sponge to draw the excess water from the tray.

 RULES OF THUMB about watering: Large plants transpire more than small ones. Maintain good ventilation. Check the soil of each plant for moisture. This will be a base to work from in developing your watering skill.

Signs of over watering are: curly, yellow leaves, constant soggy soil, fungus, and slow growth. Over watering may affect a plant and the inexperienced gardener might not see any flagrant symptoms for a long time.

Under-watering is less of a problem. However, it is common in smaller pots. Small containers dry out quickly and may need daily watering. If forgotten, the poor water-starved plant is stunted.

Most gardeners panic when they see their beautiful garden wilted in bone-dry soil.

If the soil is nearly or completely dry, take the following steps: Add a few drops (one drop per pint) of a biodegradable, concentrated liquid soap such as Castile or Ivory concentrate to the water. It will act as a wetting agent, helping the water penetrate soil more efficiently and guard against dry soil pockets. Most soluble fertilizers contain a wetting agent. Apply about a fourth to half as much water/fertilizer as the plant is expected to need. Wait 10 to 15 minutes for it to totally soak in, then apply more water/fertilizer until the soil is evenly moist. If trays are underneath the pots, let excess water remain in the trays a few hours or even overnight before removing it with a large turkey baster.

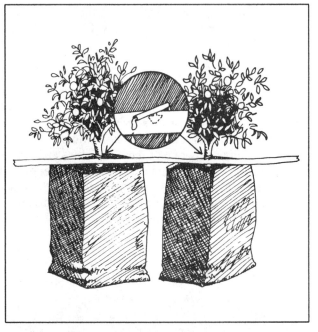

An inexpensive drip watering system makes watering a snap.

A readily accessible water source is very convenient; it saves time and labor. A 10-by-10-foot garden, containing 24 healthy tomato, pepper and cucumber plants in six-gallon pots, could need 10 to 30 gallons of water per week. Water weighs eight pounds a gallon. Thirty gallons X eight pounds = 240 pounds! That's a lot of containers to fill, lift and spill. Carrying water in containers from the bathroom sink to the garden is all right when plants are small, but when they get large, it is a big, sloppy, regular job. Running a hose into the garden saves much labor and mess. A lightweight, half-inch hose easy to handle and is less prone to damage plants. The water source should have hot and cold water running out the same tap and be equipped with threads. A hose may easily be attached and tepid water used to water the garden. A dishwasher coupling can be used if the faucet has no threads. The hose should have an on/off valve at the outlet, so water flow can be controlled while watering. A rigid watering wand will save many broken branches when you're leaning over to water in tight quarters. Wands are found at the nursery or constructed from plastic PVC pipe. Do not leave water under pressure in the hose. Garden hose is meant to transport water, not hold it under pressure, which may cause it to rupture.

To make a siphon or gravity-fed watering system, place a barrel at least 4 feet high in the grow room. If humidity is a problem, put a lid on the barrel or move it to another room. The attic is a good place because it warms the water and promotes good pressure. Place a siphon hose in the top of the tank or install a PVC on/off valve near the bottom of the barrel. An inexpensive device that measures the gallons of water added to the barrel can be purchased at most hardware stores. It is easy to walk off and let the barrel overflow. A shut-off float valve can also be installed in the barrel so there is a constant supply of water.

Fertilizer

Most flowers and vegetables grow so fast under HID lamps that ordinary potting soil can not supply all necessary nutrients for rapid, healthy growth. Fertilizing is necessary to make extra nutrients available for sustained vigorous growth.

There are about 16 elements known to be necessary for plant life. Carbon, hydrogen and oxygen are absorbed from the air and water. The rest of the elements, called nutrients, are absorbed mainly from the soil or fertilizer. The primary nutrients (nitrogen (N), phosphorus (P) and potassium (K)) are the elements a plant uses the most. Almost all fertilizers show the N-P-K percentages in big numbers on the front of the package. They are always listed in the same N-P-K order. For example, a 23-19-17 fertilizer has 23 percent nitrogen, 19 percent phosphorus and 17 percent potassium.

Calcium (Ca) and magnesium (Mg) are secondary nutrients or elements. They are sometimes classified with N-P-K as macro-nutrients. Iron (Fe), sulfur (S), manganese (Mn), boron (B), molybdenum (Mo), zinc (Zn) and copper (Cu) are trace elements

or micro-nutrients. Trace elements are usually found in sufficient quantities in potting soil and in complete fertilizers such as Peters and Ecogrow for healthy plant growth and do not need to be added. Unless fortified, soilless mixes may be severely lacking in secondary and trace elements. It is still a good idea to use a fertilizer containing trace elements. Secondary and trace elements are usually not listed on fertilizer labels.

Primary Nutrients

Nitrogen (N) is the most important nutrient. It regulates the plant's ability to make proteins, essential to new protoplasm in the cells. Nitrogen is essential to the production of chlorophyll and is mainly responsible for leaf and stem growth as well as overall size and vigor. Nitrogen is most active in young buds, shoots and leaves. Annuals love nitrogen and require high levels during vegetative growth.

Phosphorus (P) is necessary for photosynthesis and provides a mechanism for energy transfer within the plant. Phosphorus is associated with overall vigor and seed production. Plants use highest levels of phosphorus during the germination, seedling, and flowering stages of growth.

Potassium (K) or potash (K_2O) is essential to the manufacture and movement of sugars and starches, as well as growth by cell division. Potassium increases chlorophyll in foliage and helps regulate stomata openings so plants make better use of light and air. Potash encourages strong root growth and is associated with disease resistance and water intake. Potassium is necessary during all stages of growth.

Secondary Nutrients

Magnesium (Mg) is found as a central atom in every chlorophyll molecule. It is essential to the absorption of light energy. Magnesium aids in the utilization of nutrients. It also neutralizes soil acids and toxic compounds produced by the plant. Calcium is fundamental to cell manufacture and growth. Plants must have some calcium at the growing tip of each root.

Trace elements are essential to chlorophyll formation and must be present in minute amounts, but little is known about the exact amounts that are needed. They function mainly as catalysts to plant processes.

Fertilizers

The goal of fertilizing is to supply the plant with proper amounts of nutrients for vigorous growth without toxifying the soil by over-fertilizing. A five- or six-gallon container full of rich, fertile potting soil will supply all the necessary nutrients for a month or longer. After the roots have absorbed most of the available macro-nutrients, they must be added to the soil to sustain vigorous growth. Unless fortified, soilless mixes require N-P-K fertilization from the start. I like to start fertilizing fortified soilless mixes after the first week or two of growth. Most commercial soilless mixes are fortified with secondary and trace elements. Use a complete fertilizer containing secondary and trace elements in mixes that are not fortified.

A plant has different fertilizer needs as its metabolism changes throughout life. During germination and seedling growth, intake of phosphorus is high. The vegetative growth stage requires high amounts of nitrogen for green leaf growth. phosphorus and potassium are also necessary in substantial levels; a general-purpose N-P-K fertilizer is recommended. In the flowering stage, the plant is less concerned with vegetative growth. phosphorus intake is highest; nitrogen and potassium are less important. Using a super bloom fertilizer, low in nitrogen and potassium, and high in phosphorus will promote larger flowers. However, some gardeners use an N-P-K, general-purpose fertilizer and get acceptable results. A high nitrogen content usually promotes greener, leafy growth during flowering. Plants need some nitrogen during flowering. Without nitrogen, older foliage may yellow and die prematurely.

Fertilizers are either (water) soluble or gradual release. Both soluble and gradual release fertilizers can be organic or chemical.

Soluble fertilizers lend themselves to indoor container cultivation. They are preferred by commercial nurserypersons and many indoor gardeners. Soluble fertilizers dissolve in water and can be added or washed (leached) out of the soil easily. It is easy to control the exact amount of nutrients available to plants in a soluble form. Versatile soluble fertilizer can be applied in a water solution to the soil or misted directly on the leaves. Foliar feeding supplies nutrients directly to the leaves where they are used.

Chemical Soluble Fertilizers can be granular fertilizers or liquid. The granular fertilizers can easily be over-applied, creating toxic soil. It is almost impossible to leach them out fast enough to save the plant.

Osmocote™ chemical fertilizers are time-release. They are used by many nurseries because they are easy to apply and require only one application every few months. Using this type of fertilizer may be convenient, but exacting control is lost. Osmocote is best suited for ornamental containerized plants when labor costs and uniform growth are the main concerns.

Peters™ fertilizer has been the choice of professional nurserypeople for many years. Indoor gardeners love it because the salts are pure and easy to work with. It is formulated with chelating agents to prevent settling out of elements, contains necessary secondary and trace elements. Peters has no chloride carbonates or excess sulfates, preventing buildup of excess salts. It is excellent for use with both soil and soilless mixes. Peters comes in many different N-P-K formulas. Those most commonly used indoors are listed.

The following Peters formulas are mixed from a half-tablespoon to a tablespoon per gallon of water and applied with each watering.

General Purpose (20-20-20) is readily available at most nurseries and used during the seedling and vegetative stages*.

Peat-Lite Special (20-10-20) works very well during vegetative growth in both soil and soilless mixes. Less phosphorus helps contain roots. It contains high levels of secondary and trace nutrients**.

Geranium Special (15-15-15), also used during vegetative growth, works very well for low pH situations. Geranium Special has a non-acidic source of nitrogen and reduced ammonium toxicity potential**.

Blossom Booster (10-30-20) contains a high level of phosphorus, which is necessary during flowering. It increases bud set, count and size**.

Variegated Violet Special (5-50-17) offers an accepted method of holding variegation in a plant's leaves. It reduces nitrogen, greatly increases phosphorus and holds a minimum potassium level. Some gardeners use it as a "super bloom" fertilizer.

*Trace elements: magnesium .05%, iron .05%, manganese .0031%, boron .0068%, zinc .0025%, copper .0036%, molybdenum .0009%

**Trace element content: magnesium .15%, iron .10%, manganese .056%, boron .02%, zinc .0162%, copper .01%, molybdenum .01%

Ecogrow[R] is produced in Seattle by Eco Enterprises. Its various formulas are made with the hydroponic horticulturist in mind, but can be used with soil too. Ecogrow is a balanced formula that gives plants all of the nutrients necessary for strong, healthy growth. All the elements in Ecogrow are derived from natural minerals. Nothing artificial is added. One of the interesting qualities of Ecogrow is that it does not totally dissolve in the nutrient solution. There are enough nutrients in the solution that plants get properly nourished. Do not worry about a little sediment in the solution. The pH is balanced at 6.3 when mixed with neutral tap water.

All Ecogrow and bloom formulas contain secondary and trace element analysis: Calcium 6%, sulfur 2.6%, magnesium 2.0%, iron .2%, Mn .1%, Cl .1%, copper .005%, zinc .05%, boron .045%, molybdenum .002% .001% copper.

Standard (10-8-14) - a general-purpose fertilizer formulated for vegetative growth.
Monstera (20-6-12) - for plants needing high nitrogen intake for rapid vegetative growth.
Bloom (3-35-10) - blossom-boosting formula low in nitrogen and high in phosphorus; great for fat, healthy, strong buds.
Eco "R" formulas are made specially for use with rockwool. The two part formula is loved by a multitude of home gardeners.

Miracle-Gro[R] is the old reliable house plant and vegetable food. It comes in several formulas and may be found at just about any store with a gardening section. Miracle-Gro lists secondary and trace elements on the guaranteed analysis panel: copper .05%, chelated iron .10%, manganese .05%, and zinc .05%.
Tomato (18-18-21) formula also contains magnesium .05%. Many vegetables and flowers have very similar nutrient requirements. This formula is great for seedling and vegetative growth.
All-Purpose (15-30-15) formula is preferred by gardeners during flowering. The high concentration of phosphorus helps rapid bud formation.

Hydrolife is a favorite complete hydroponic fertilizer in the Northwest. This fertilizer no amonical nitrogen. Nitrate nigrogen provides a a constant source of available nitrogen. This fertilizer is especially good in NFT gardens

Grow (9-7-14) consists of two granular parts that are mixed together with water. Grow contains a balanced mix of all necessary trace elements including: magnesium, sulphur, boron, cobalt, copper, iron, manganese, molybdenum, zinc and calcium.
Bloom (0-7-5) is a liquid concentrate that is actually a third ingredient which is mixed with the *Grow* discribed above. The combination of *Grow* and *Bloom* form a complete flowering formula.

General Hydroponics offers three separate formulas (*FloraGro, FloraMicro*, and *FloraBloom*) that can be used to construct your own specific formula for seedlings, vegetative growth and flowering plants. PH buffering agents keep the acid-to-alkaline-balance entact so that nutrients are always available.

The developer of this formula, Larry Brook, has completed extensive hydroponic experiements. Larry's formula is one of the best on the market.

Jungle Juice, manufactured by Hydrolights in Northern California, is derived from purely organic substances. The liquid concentrate is easily diluted in water to form an excellent available mix.

Formula One is a two part formula. It is based on vegetable fertilizer formulas used in Dutch greenhouse growers. This liquid fertilizer concentrate dilutes readily in water. It is one of the best formulas available for vegetable production.

Dutch Magic Nutrient is the result of numerous trips to Holland, scouring the country for that special formula used by greenhouse growers.

Higher Yield garden center in Tacoma, Washington developed this fertilizer mix. It is easy to dilute and the pH is easy to control. Many growers love this mix.

General Hydroponics formulas.

Organic Fertilizers

Organic plants boast a sweeter taste, but implementing an organic indoor garden requires horticultural know-how. The limited soil, space and the necessity for sanitation must be considered when growing organically. Outdoors, organic gardening is easy because all the forces of nature are there for you to seek out and harness. Indoors, essentially none of the natural phenomena are at play. Remember, you are Mother Nature and must create everything! The nature of growing indoors does not lend itself to long-term organic gardens, but some organic techniques have been practiced successfully.

Most indoor organic gardens use potting soil, rich in worm castings, peat, sand, manure, leaf mold, compost and fine dolomite lime. In a container, there is little or no space to build the soil by mixing composts and organic nutrients to cook down. Even if it were possible to build soil in a container, it would take months of valuable growing time. It is easiest and safest to throw old, depleted soil outdoors and start new plants with fresh organic soil.

Organic nutrients, manure, worm castings, blood and bone meal etc. work very well to increase the soil's nutrient content, but nutrients are released and available at different rates. The nutrient availability may be difficult to calculate, but it is hard to over-apply organic fertilizers. Organic nutrients work best when used in combination with one another. This gives a more consistent availability of nutrients. A mix of 20 to 40 percent worm castings with other organic amendments yields a strong, readily available nitrogen base. A later application bat guano boosts flowering.

An indoor garden using raised beds allows true organic methods. The raised bed has enough soil to hold nutrients, promote chemical activity, and ensure a constant supply of nutrients.

Material	N	P	K	Notes
Blood (dried or meal)	12-15	1.2	1	soluble
Bone meal (unsteamed	2-4	15	25	calcium, TE
Bone meal (steamed)	2-3	18-25	.2	20% Ca, TE
Canola meal	0	1.2	1.3	iron, TE
Cottonseed meal	7	2	2	acidic
Poultry manure (dry)	3-4	2-4	1-2	soluble, TE
Compost	1-2	1	1	TE
Cow (steer) manure	.6-2	.3	.5-1	excess salts
Coffee grounds	2	.3	.7	acidic
Feathers (dry or meal)	12-15	0	0	some TE
Fish meal	8	7	2	soluble
Goat manure	.5	.4	.4	TE
Granite dust	0	0	4-5	some TE
Potash rock	0	6-8	0	some TE
Greensand (glauconite)	-	1	5-7	iron, Mg., TE
Guano (bat)	2-5	8-10	1-2	soluble, TE
Guano (seabird)	10-15	5	2	soluble, TE
Hoof & horn meal	6-15	2	0	TE
Horse manure	.6	.4	.4	TE
Paper ash	0	.1	2-3	high pH
Soft phosphate	0	18-24	0	calcium, TE
Seaweed (liquid)	.5	.5	.3	soluble, TE
Seaweed (meal)	1	1	1	soluble, TE
Sheep manure	.8	.4	.5	TE
Swine manure	.6	.4	.2	TE
Wood ash (hardwood)	0	1.5	7-10	soluble
Wood ash (softwood)	0	.8	5	soluble
Worm castings	3.5	1	1	TE

TE = Trace elements

The nutrients in organic fertilizers may vary greatly depending upon source, age, erosion, climate, etc. The above figures are only approximate. For exact nutrient content, consult the vendor's specifications.

The Tea Bag

Five- or 10-gallon pots do not contain enough soil to hold all the organic nutrients a plant will need throughout life. This dilemma is solved by using organic tea. The tea is a bit messy, even smelly, but very effective. Tea concoctions contain just about any soluble organic nutrient diluted in water.

Worm castings and chicken manure, high in nitrogen, and bat guano, high in phosphorus, are the most common ingredients in U-mix organic teas. These soluble nutrients are immediately available to plants. There are many different mixtures of organic tea. Just mix the organic nutrient(s) with water; let it sit overnight. Mix it again, then strain out the heavy stuff by pouring the solution through a cheesecloth or an old nylon stocking before applying. The tea may be applied as often as each watering.

The growth or yield attained by using either chemical or organic fertilizers is about the same. However, in the long run, organic fertilizers are much more productive than chemicals. The chemical fertilizers do not build soil and can build up to toxic proportions quickly. Organic fertilizers on the other hand, continually build the soil, promote better texture and structure and foster soil organism growth. The addition of organic fertilizers over a long period enhances the soil life and unlike chemicals does not contribute to its sterility.

Plants must convert organic nutrients to a chemical form before they are useable. This chemical change happens regardless of the source of the nutrients.

"Semi-organic" and "organically based" fertilizers are not actually organic fertilizers. They normally supplement these mixes with superphosphate and potassium sulfate.

Bone, kelp, and seed meals in 40 to 50 pound sacks are more difficult to find at retail nurseries, but man be found at farm-supply stores.

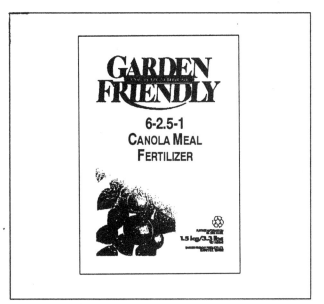

Garden Friendly packages one of the most popular lines of organic fertilizer on the West Coast.

Alfalfa Meal is rich in nitrogen, containing about 2.5 percent and .5 percent phosphorus and about 2 percent potash.

Blood (dried or meal) is collected at slaughterhouses, dried and ground into a powder or meal. It is an excellent source of fast-acting soluble nitrogen (12 to 15 percent by weight), about 1.2 percent phosphorus and under one percent potash. Apply just before planting or as a side dressing to stimulate green leafy growth. It can burn plants if set on foliage or applied to heavily. Blood meal attracts meat-eating animals, so always cultivate it into the soil if using as a side dressing.

Bone meal is an old time fertilizer that is rich in phosphorus and nitrogen. The age and type of bone determine the nutrient content of this pulverized slaughterhouse product. Older bones have a higher phosphorus content than young bones. Use bone meal in conjunction with other organic fertilizers for best results. It's lime content helps reduce soil acidity and acts fastest in well-aerated soil.

Raw, unsteamed bone meal contains 2 to 4 percent nitrogen and 15 to 25 percent phosphorus. Fatty acids in raw bone meal requires longer to decompose. This meal is most commonly used as a phosphorus source when planting fall bulbs.

Steamed or cooked bone meal is made from fresh animal bones that have been boiled or steamed under pressure to render out fats. The pressure treatment causes a little nitrogen loss and an increase in phosphorus. Steamed bones are easier to grind into a fine powder and the process helps nutrients become available sooner. It contains up to 30 percent phosphorus and about 1.5 percent nitrogen. The finer bone meal is ground, the faster acting. Apply as a seasonal source of phosphorus to the soil when planting or to enhance flowers and fruit set as a mid summer top dressing that is lightly cultivated into the soil and covered with mulch.

Cottonseed meal is made from shelled cotton seed that has had the oil extracted. Virtually all chemical residues from commercial cotton production are dissolved in the oil. This acidic fertilizer contains about 7 percent nitrogen, 2.5 percent phosphorus and 1.5 percent potash. It should be supplemented with rock phosphate or bone meal to form a balanced fertilizer blend.

Cottonseed meal is an excellent food for acid-loving plants.

Chicken manure is a favorite of many gardeners because it is so high in nitrogen. If you can find a good source of chicken manure, get as much as you can. Pile it up next to the compost pile, let it rot for a couple of months then cover it with a tarp to slow decomposition. Use it as a compost activator, a top or side dressing as often as possible. If the manure comes from a commercial chicken ranch that uses growth hormones, let it compost at least a year so the hormones are washed out or "fixed". Many times chicken manure is full of feathers that contain as much as 17 percent nitrogen which is an added bonus.

The average nutrient content of wet chicken manure is: N - 1.5%, P - 1.5%, K - 0.5% and dry: N - 4%, P - 4%, K - 1.5% and both have a full range of trace elements.

Compost tea is used by numerous organic gardeners as the only source of fertilizer. Comfrey is packed with nutrients and many gardeners grow it just to make a compost tea.

Cow manure is sold as "steer manure" but it is collected from dairy herds. Gardeners have used cow manure for centuries and this has led to the belief that it is a good fertilizer as well as a soil amendment.

Steer manure is most valuable as a mulch and a soil amendment; holds water well and maintains fertility for a long time. The nutrient value is quite low and should not be relied upon for the main source of nitrogen.

The average nutrient content of cow manure is N - .6%, P - 0.3%, K - 0.3% and a full range of trace elements. Apply at the rate of 25-30 pounds per square yard.

Coffee grounds are acidic and encourage acetic-acid-bacteria in the soil. Drip coffee grounds are the richest containing about 2 percent nitrogen and traces of other nutrients. Add to the compost pile or scatter and cultivate in as a top dressing around acid loving azaleas, blueberries, camelias and rhododendrons.

Diatomaceous earth, the fossilized skeletal remains of fresh and salt water algae, contains a full range of trace elements and is a good insecticide. Apply to the soil when cultivating or as a top dressing.

Dolomite lime adjusts and balances the pH and makes phosphates more available. Generally applied to "sweeten" or de-acidify soil. It consists of calcium and magnesium, sometimes listed as primary nutrients but generally referred to as the secondary nutrients. See page 52 for more information.

Feathers and feather meal contain from 12 to 15 percent nitrogen that is released slowly. Feathers included in barnyard chicken manure or obtained from slaughterhouses, are an excellent addition to the compost pile or as a fertilizer. Feathers are steamed under pressure, dried, then ground into a powdery feather meal. Feather meal contains a slow-release nitrogen of about 12.5 percent. Apply in the fall with cover crops for nitrogen-rich soil the following spring.

Fish meal is made from dried fish that is ground into a meal. It is rich in nitrogen (about 8 percent) and contains around 7 percent phosphoric acid and many trace elements. It has an unpleasant odor and should not be used indoors. A great compost activator. Apply to the soil as a relatively fast-acting side or top dressing; make sure to cultivate it into the soil or cover with mulch after applying. Always store in an air tight container so it will not attract cats, dogs and flies.

Fish meal and fish emulsion can contain up to 10 percent nitrogen. The liquid generally contains less nitrogen than the meal. Even when deodorized, the liquid form has an unpleasant odor.

Inorganic potash is added by some manufacturers and is "semi-organic."

Fish emulsion, an inexpensive soluble liquid, is high in organic nitrogen, trace elements and some phosphorus and potassium. This natural fertilizer is difficult to over-apply and is immediately available to plants. Fish emulsion may be diluted with water and used as a foliar spray, but may clog small nozzles if mixed too rich. Even deodorized fish emulsion smells. Use only on outdoor plants.

Goat manure is much like horse manure but more potent. Compost this manure and treat it as you would horse manure.

Granite dust or granite stone meal contains up to 5 percent potash and several trace elements. Releasing nutrients slowly over several years, granite dust is an inexpensive source of potash and does not affect soil pH. Apply as a top dressing or at the rate of ten to fifteen pounds per 100 square feet. Combine granite dust with phosphate rock and manure for a complete fertilizer mix to start crops in the spring.

Potash rock supplies up to 8 percent potassium and may contain many trace elements.

Greensand (glaucomite) is an iron potassium silicate that gives the minerals in which it occurs a green tent. It is mined from an ancient New Jersey sea bed deposits of shells and organic material rich in iron phosphorus, potash (5 to 7 percent) and numerous micronutrients. Some organic gardeners do not use greensand because it is such a limited resource. Greensand does not burn plants, slowly releasing its treasures in about four years. Apply liberal amounts of greensand as a top dressing or blend with soil at the rate of 15 to 25 pounds per 100 square feet any time of year as a long-term source of potassium and trace elements.

Guano (bat) consists of the droppings and remains of bats. It is rich in soluble nitrogen, phosphorus and trace elements. The limited supply of this fertilizer, known as the soluble organic super bloom, makes it somewhat expensive. Mined in sheltered caves, guano dries with minimal decomposition. Bat guano can be thousands of years old. Newer deposits contain high levels of nitrogen and are capable of burning if applied too heavily. The more popular older deposits are high in phosphorus and make an excellent flowering fertilizer. Bat guano is usually powdery and used any time of year as a top dressing or diluted in a tea and used as a foliar spray. Do not breathe the dust when handling; it can cause nausea and irritation. Bats are too often associated with rabies and horror movies. Only ten cases of rabies have been reported in the U.S. from bat bites. Some bats eat thousands of insects nightly, others rotting fruit. These prehistoric descendents are invaluable to the ecosystem and should be protected as our friends. Bat guano may be difficult to find at retail stores; however, several suppliers listed in *The Growing Edge Magazine* stock bat guano.

Guano (sea bird) is high in nitrogen and other nutrients. The Humboldt Current along the coast of Peru and northern Chile keeps the rain from falling, and decomposition of the guano is minimal. South American guano is among the world's best. The guano is scraped off the rocks of arid sea islands. The average dose is one tablespoon per gallon of water. Guano is also collected from many coastlines around the world.

Gypsum, hydrated calcium sulfate, is used to lower soil pH and improve drainage and aeration. It is also used to hold or slow the rapid decomposition of nitrogen.

Hoof and horn meal is a coarse granular substance that is an excellent source of slow-release nitrogen. The drawback of meal is that it draws flies and encourages maggots. Soil bacteria must break it down before it is available to roots. Apply two to three weeks before planting. It remains in soil for six months or longer. Hoof and horn meal contains from 6 to 15 percent nitrogen and about 2 percent phosphoric acid. Finely ground horn meal, on the other hand, makes the nitrogen available quicker and has few problems with fly maggots.

Horse manure is readily available from horse stables and race tracks. Use horse manure that has straw or peat for bedding; wood shavings could be a source of plant disease.

Compost horse manure for two months or more before adding to the garden. The composting process kills weed seeds and it will make better use of the nutrients. Straw bedding may also use up much of the available nitrogen. But the straw makes a lot of air space within the manure so it can be piled quite high without adding other materials to provide ventilation. In fact, stomping the manure down as you stack it will drive out extra air spaces so that it will hold more water necessary for composting.

Nutrient content of horse manure N - 0.6%, P - 0.6%, K - 0.4% and a full range of trace elements.

Kelp is the "Cadillac of trace minerals." Kelp should be deep green, fresh and smell like the ocean. Seaweed contains 60 to 70 trace minerals that are already chelated (existing in a form that's water-soluble and mobile in the soil).

Oyster shells are ground and normally used as a calcium source for poultry. They contain up to 55 percent calcium and traces of many other nutrients that release slowly. Add ground oyster shells to compost or in small amounts with other fertilizers when cultivating to ensure adequate calcium content.

Paper ash contains about 5% phosphorus and over 2% potash. It is an excellent water soluble fertilizer, but do not apply in large doses because the pH is quite high.

Pigeon manure has a very high concentration of nitrogen but is more difficult to find. It can be used in the same fashion as chicken manure.

Rabbit manure is also excellent fertilizer but is difficult to find in large quantities. Use rabbit manure as you would chicken or pigeon manure.

Rock phosphate (hard) is a calcium or lime based phosphate rock that is finely ground to the consistency of talcum powder. This rock powder contains over 30 percent phosphate and a menagerie of trace elements. It does not leach out of the soil, remaining unchanged until taken up by roots. Apply at the rate of ten pounds per 100 square feet of soil or turf grass every four or five years a couple of months after applying annual manure.

Colloidal phosphate, also called powdered or soft phosphate, which is a natural clay phosphate deposit that contains just over 20 percent phosphorus (P_2O_5), calcium and many trace elements. Colloidal phosphate is an excellent value in organic fertilizers. It yields 2 percent phosphate by weight the first season and a total of 18 percent over the next several years. Soft phosphate will not burn and is available to plants as they needed. It is also a good soil builder that encourages earthworms and beneficial soil microbes. Cultivate soft phosphate into the soil annually at the rate of five pounds per 100 square feet of soil or turf grass piles in conjunction with lime and nitrogen-rich manures and seaweed meal. Or till in 15 to 20 pounds of soft phosphate per 100 square feet along with lime every four years.

Rock potash is an important source of potassium. It releases very slowly and stays in the soil for several years.

Seaweed meal or kelp meal is harvested from the ocean or picked up along beaches, cleansed of salty water, dried and ground into a powdery meal. It is packed full of potassium (potash) numerous trace elements, vitamins, amino acids and plant hormones. The nutrient content varies according to the type of kelp and its growing conditions. Seaweed meal is easily assimilated by plants and contributes to soil life, structure and nitrogen fixation. It may also help plants resist many diseases and withstand light frosts. Apply the dry powder at the rate of one or two pounds per 100 square feet of garden soil or lawn in the spring for best results, but it can be applied any time. Allow several weeks for soil bacteria to make nutrients available. Kelp meal is also speeds compost decomposition and eases transplant shock.

Seaweed (liquid) contains nitrogen, phosphorus, potash, all necessary trace elements that are chelated (existing in a form that's water-soluble and mobile in the soil) and plant hormones. Apply dilute solution to the soil or use as a foliar spray for a quick cure of nutrient deficiencies. Liquid seaweed is also great for soaking seeds and dipping cuttings or bare roots before planting.

Sheep manure is normally found indoors in the sheep pens. It is high in nutrients and makes a wonderful tea. The average nutrient content is: N - 0.8%, P - 0.5%, K - 0.4% and a full range of trace elements.

Sheep manures are hot because they contain little water and lots of air. They heat up readily in a compost pile. Cow and pig manures are cold because they hold a lot of water and can be compacted easily, squeezing out the air.

Shrimp & crab wastes contain relatively high levels of phosphorus.

Sulfate of potash is normally produced chemically by treating rock powders with sulfuric acid, but one company, Great Salt Lake Minerals and Chemicals Company produces a concentrated natural form. The sulfate of potash is extracted from the Great Salt Lake.

Swine manure has a high nutrient content but is slower acting and wetter than cow and horse manure. The average nutrient content of pig manure is: N - 0.6%, P - 0.6%, K - 0.4% and a full range of trace elements.

Wood ashes (hardwood) supply up to 10 percent potash and softwood ashes contain about 5 percent. Potash leaches rapidly, so collect ash soon after burning and store in a dry place. Apply in a mix with other fertilizers at the rate of five or ten pounds per 100 square feet. The potash washes out of heavy layers of wood ash quickly and cause compacted, sticky soil. Avoid using wood ashes, which are highly alkaline, around azaleas, blueberries, camelias, rhododendrons and other acid-loving plants. Wood ash makes an excellent addition to compost piles.

Worm castings are digested humus and other organic matter that contain varying amounts of N-P-K. They are an excellent source of non-burning soluble nitrogen that is available immediately. Worm castings are also an excellent soil additive that promote fertility and soil structure. Mix with potting soil to form a rich, fertile blend. Worm castings, when pure, look like coarse graphite powder. They are high in available nitrogen as well as many other nutrients. Worm castings are used as an organic fertilizer and soil amendment. Earthworms eat and digest decomposing organic matter. The castings are this excreted organic matter. Worm castings are heavy and very dense. When mixing with soil, use no more than 30 percent worm castings. They are so heavy, root growth can be impaired. Worm castings vary in the amount of nitrogen they contain. Most nurseries do not stock worm castings. However, there are many people making their own. Check the newspaper and ask at the nursery for possible sources.

Note: The nutrients in organic fertilizers may vary greatly depending upon source, age, erosion, climate, etc. For exact nutrient content, consult the vendor's specifications.

Transplanting, Seedling and Cutting Fertilizers

Vitamin B_1 is recommended for a smooth move of cuttings, transplants, and seedling growth. There are many similar products that work just as well or better. Vitamin B_1 helps ease transplant wilt and shock. Using vitamin B_1 makes transplanting fast and easy.

A mild manure tea that is made from guano, manure and some form of seaweed make excellent seedling fertilizers. Remember that seedlings have few roots and are very frail. Always give them half or quarter strength fertilizer tea.

Trace Element Fertilizers

Seaweed, either liquid or powdered, is packed with trace elements that are immediately available to plants. Seaweed is the number one trace element fertilizer of environmentally conscious gardeners.

Compound 111, S.T.E.M. and FTE are all Peters[R] products. Many other companies, both local and national, produce excellent products that are similar to Peters'. These trace element formulas are used by many indoor gardeners and nurserypeople alike. They work well to alleviate any trace element deficiency except for magnesium. None of the formulations contain any magnesium.

Compound 111 is a supplemental formula containing trace elements (iron 1.5%, manganese .12%, zinc .0754%, copper .11362%, boron .23242%, molybdenum .1075%) chelating agents, penetrating agents and color tracers. This formula is highly recommended if you mix your own fertilizer out of single elements or are using a fertilizer that does not contain trace elements. Compound 111 is the easiest trace element formula to use and the safest. It has less of each element to toxify the soil, and unlike the S.T.E.M. formula, does not contain sulfur. Compound 111 works well to treat any mysterious trace element deficiency. Often there is a suspicion of trace element deficiency, but the exact deficiency is not known for sure. By applying Compound 111, the problem will be solved and you will not have to know the exact cause of the deficiency.

The S.T.E.M. (Soluble Trace Element Mix) was developed to furnish trace elements immediately, in large doses. This is one of the hottest, most potent trace element formulas available. Be very careful when using it. The S.T.E.M. formula was developed for a one-time application in treating trace element deficiencies. Note the high percentage of trace element concentrations.

The guaranteed analysis of Peters S.T.E.M. formula is: sulfur 15.0%, boron 1.45%, copper 3.20%, iron 7.5%, molybdenum 8.15%, Zinc 4.5%.

FTE (Fritted trace elements) are mixed with the soil or soilless mix for a long-lasting, slow-release application of six to 12 months. The elements are encased in a pulverized glass complex that resists heavy leaching. The nutrients are available at a more constant rate throughout life. This is a form of gradual release fertilizer, and is the only one that I recommend. The FTE formula is safer to use than the soluble formulas, but may be overdone also. Once overdone, FTE may not be leached out. Apply only one-third teaspoon per cubic foot of soil.

The guaranteed analysis of Peters FTE is: molybdenum 5.0%, iron 14.0%, copper 1.5%, zinc 5.0%, boron 0.8%, molybdenum 0.07%.

Mixing

To mix, dissolve powder, crystals, or liquid into a little warm (90 to 100^0 F, 32 to 38^0 C) water; make sure it is totally dissolved, then add the balance of the tepid water. This practice will ensure that the fertilizer and water mix evenly.

Containers have very little soil in which to hold nutrients. Toxic salt buildup may become a problem. Follow dosage instructions to the letter. Adding too much fertilizer will not make plants grow faster. It may change the chemical balance of the soil and supply too much of a nutrient or lock in other nutrients, making them unavailable to the plant.

Fertilizing

Do plants need fertilization? This may be determined by visual inspection, making an N-P-K soil test, or experimenting on a test plant(s). No matter which method is used, remember that plants in small containers use available nutrients quickly and need frequent fertilizing; plants in large planters have more soil, have more nutrients, and require less frequent fertilizing.

Visual inspection: If plants are growing well and have deep green, healthy leaves, they are probably getting all necessary nutrients from the soil. The moment growth slows, or leaves begin to turn pale green, it is time to fertilize. Do not confuse yellow leaves caused by a lack of light and yellow leaves caused by a nutrient deficiency.

Making an N-P-K soil test will reveal exactly how much of each major nutrient is available to the plant. The test kits mix a soil sample with a chemical. After the soil settles, a color reading is taken from the liquid, then matched to a color chart. The appropriate percentage of fertilizer is then added. This method is very exact, but more trouble than it is worth for most hobby gardeners.

Many gardeners prefer to experiment on two or three test plants. This method yields experience and develops horticultural skills. Cuttings work especially well for this type of experiment. Give the test plants some fertilizer and see if they green up and grow faster.

Dissolved salts (DS) meters, also referred to as electrical conductivity (EC) meters, are fundamental to precise control of overall nutrient content in the growing medium.

Once it has been determined that the plants need fertilizer, but how much? The answer is simple. Just mix fertilizer as per instructions and water as normal, or dilute fertilizer and apply more often. If you want to get the most out of fertilization, use a soluble salts meter. Remember, small plants use much less fertilizer than large ones. Fertilize early in the day, so plants have all day to absorb and process the fertilizer.

It is almost impossible to explain how often to apply fertilizer. We know that large plants use more nutrients than small plants. The more often fertilizer is applied, the less concentrated it should be. Frequency of fertilization is one of the most widely disagreed upon subjects in the horticultural industry. Indoor, containerized plants may be pushed to incredible lengths. Some of them will absorb amazing amounts of fertilizer and grow well. Many gardeners add as much as one tablespoon per gallon (Peters 20-20-20 or 10-30-20) with each watering! Heavy fertilization works best with growing mediums, especially soilless mix, that drain readily and are easy to leach. Other gardeners use only rich organic potting soil with fine dolomite lime added. No supplemental fertilizer is applied at all.

A siphon applicator found at most nurseries will mix soluble fertilizers with water. The applicator is attached to the faucet with the siphon hose submerged in the concentrated fertilizer solution. The hose is attached to the other end. Often applicators are set at a 1:15 ratio. That is, for every unit of liquid concentrate fertilizer, 15 units of water will be mixed with it. Sufficient water flow is necessary for the suction to work properly. Misting nozzles restrict this flow. When the water is turned on, the fertilizer is siphoned into the system and flows out the hose. Fertilizer is generally applied with each watering, since a small percentage of fertilizer is metered in.

A garbage can, set 3 to 4 inches off the floor with a garden hose fitting at the bottom, will act as a gravity-flow source for fertilizer solution. The container is filled with water and fertilizer. With this system, the water temperature is easy to keep warm and fertilization is much easier.

When it comes to fertilization, experience will tell more than anything else. There are hundreds of N-P-K mixes and they all work! When choosing a fertilizer, make sure to read the entire label and know what the fertilizer claims it can do. Do not be afraid to try a few test plants.

Once you have an idea of how often to fertilize, put the garden on a regular feeding schedule of biweekly, weekly, bimonthly, every watering, every other watering or every third watering. A schedule usually works very well, but it must be combined with a vigilant, caring eye that looks for over-fertilization and signs of nutrient deficiency.

 RULE OF THUMB: Leach soil with one to two gallons of fresh water per gallon of soil every month or two. This is the best form of preventive maintenance against toxic salt buildup in the soil. Leaching too often (weekly) washes all the nutrients out of the soil.

Foliar Feeding

Foliar feeding (misting the leaves with fertilizer solution) makes some nutrients available and usable immediately. Food is absorbed directly into the leaves. Foliar feeding is a good way to keep toxic nutrient levels from building up in the soil, but, like soil fertilization, may be overdone. In general, apply all foliar fertilizers at half strength. Daily foliar feeding with a weak solution, for example, leaches the nutrients from the leaves, just

as excessive watering leaches nutrients from the soil. A good foliar feeding program would start after the plant's first month of growth. Apply fertilizer solution with a fine spray. See "About Spraying," pages 116-118.

Foliar feeding is the quickest way to deliver nutrients to a plant.

Foliar feeding is more work, but creates almost instantaneous results. Nitrogen-deficient plants have turned from a pale yellow to a lime green in 12 short hours! In the case of nutrient-deficient soil, foliar feeding is a simple quick, cure. The nutrients are supplied directly and used immediately. Soil condition and pH are not affected, but root absorption may improve. A combination of soil and foliar feeding is common. Good organic foliar fertilizers are fish emulsion and bat guano. Of course, it must be strained through a tea bag and the sprayer should not be prone to clogging. There are many chemical foliar fertilizers; Peters, and Miracle-Gro. Dilute them the same as for regular fertilization for foliar feeding.

Nutrient Disorders

There are many things which can go wrong indoors that are confused with a lack of fertilizer. The pH of both the growing medium and water is of prime importance. If the pH is not between 6 and 7 (5.4 to 6.8 for hydroponic units) some nutrients will be locked in the soil, even if the nutrient is available. The plant is not able to absorb it chemically because the pH will not let it. For example, a full point movement in pH represents a tenfold increase in either alkalinity or acidity. This means that a pH of 5.5 would be 10 times more acidic than a pH of 6.5. A pH below 6.5 may cause a deficiency in calcium. If this happens, root tips could burn and leaves could get leaf spot fungus. A pH over 7 could slow down the plant's iron intake, and chloritic leaves with yellowing veins could result.

Incorrect pH contributes to most serious nutrient disorders. Too many people worry about fertilizer application and do not pay attention to the pH! See "PH Chart," page 50.

The basic elements of the environment that must be checked. Since you are Mother Nature indoors, you are responsible for creating a perfect climate or several microclimates for the plants to grow in. Check each of the vital signs and fine tune the environment, especially the soluble salts and ventilation, before deciding that plants are nutrient-deficient.

Nutrient deficiencies do not normally occur in fresh potting soil containing dolomite lime or in a fortified soilless mix fortified that contains and containing all necessary trace elements. This fresh planting mix is coupled with a regular fertilization schedule.

Two basic problems occur with nutrients: deficiencies and excesses.

Deficiency, indicated by lime-green leaves; this is treated by applying a general-purpose fertilizer. The macro-nutrients are all used at similar rates and a single nutrient seldom builds to toxic levels. If a deficiency is suspected, leach the soil heavily. Start a new fertilization program. Adjust the pH to 6.0-7.0, and use a complete fertilizer containing all the trace elements.

Excess or overfertilization is indicated by super-dark green leaves and burnt tips; treat by leaching the soil of excess nutrients.

Over-fertilizing can become one of the biggest problems for indoor gardeners. Too much fertilizer causes a buildup of nutrients (salts) to toxic levels and changes soil chemistry. When over-fertilized, growth is rapid and super-lush green, until the toxic levels are reached. When the toxic salt (fertilizer) level is reached, leaf tips burn (turn yellow, then black) and if the problem is severe, the leaves will curl under like a bighorn sheep's horns. Over fertilization is easy to diagnose in the early stages (two or three weeks before symptoms appear) when using a soluble salts (DS) meter. For more information on the DS meter, see *Gardening: The Rockwool Book*, by George F. Van Patten.

This lime tree is being leached (flushed) with about five gallons of water to wash all the toxic salt from the soil.

The chance of over-fertilization is greater in a small amount of soil. It can hold only a small amount of nutrients. While a large pot or planter can hold much more soil and nutrients safely, it will take longer to flush if overdone.

To treat severely over-fertilized plants, leach soil with two gallons of water per gallon of soil, so as to wash all the excess nutrients out. The plant should start new growth and be looking better in one or two weeks. If the problem is severe, and leaves are curled, the soil may need to be leached several times. After the plant appears to have leveled off to normal growth, start foliar feeding or apply diluted fertilizer solution.

Primary Nutrient Disorders

Nitrogen is the most common nutrient found deficient. Growth slows; lower leaves turn yellow and eventually die. Remedy by fertilizing with nitrogen or N-P-K fertilizer. For fast results, foliar feed. An overdose of nitrogen will cause soft, weak growth, and delay flower and fruit production if it is allowed to accumulate.

Phosphorus deficiency is less common. Leaves will become deep green and uniformly smaller, and the plant will be stunted. Lower leaves will turn yellow and die. Treat with phosphorus or N-P-K fertilizer. Toxic signs of phosphorus will take a long time to surface. Treat toxicity by leaching the soil with fresh water.

Discolored leaf tips tell experiencec gardeners that toxic salt buildup is occuring and it is time to leach the soil with water.

Potassium deficiency occurs occasionally. Many times potassium deficient plants are the tallest and appear healthy. But the lower leaf tips turn yellow, followed by whole leaves that turn dark yellow and die. The potassium is usually present in the soil, but locked in by high salinity. First, leach the toxic salt out of the soil, then apply foliar N-P-K fertilizer.

Secondary Nutrient Disorders

Secondary nutrient deficiencies are easily avoided by mixing one cup of fine dolomite lime per cubic foot of soil before planting. Dolomite supplies soil with magnesium and calcium.

Magnesium (Mg) is the most common secondary nutrient to be found deficient. It is naturally deficient in soilless mixes, but is also found deficient in soil. Lower leaves yellow, veins remain green, the tips and then the entire leaf turns brown. The leaf tips usually turn upward, then die. The entire plant could discolor and die within a few weeks. Cure by watering as usual, adding one teaspoon Epsom salts to every two quarts of water. If the deficiency progresses to the top of the plant, turning the growing shoots lime-colored, you will notice the greening-up

effect there first. In a few days, it will move down the plant, turning lower leaves progressively greener. Continue a regular watering schedule with Epsom salts added until symptoms totally disappear. In a soilless mix, you may want to use Epsom salts regularly, but it will not be necessary if the fertilizer contains magnesium.

Calcium (Ca) deficiency is uncommon, but when found, it may be too late to do anything. Signs of deficiency are a yellowing and dying back of leaf edges. Mixing fine dolomite lime with the soil before planting is the best way to prevent this ailment. If you must, use a trace element formula containing calcium to treat the deficiency.

Micronutrient Disorders

Sulphur (S) is almost never a problem. Many fertilizers contain some form of sulfur. Deficiency shows when leaves turn pale green and general-purpose N-P-K fertilizer fails to cure the problem. Very seldom is it a problem, but if it is, remedy with trace element fertilizer.

Iron (Fe) deficiency is somewhat common indoors. An iron-deficient (chloritic) plant is yellowing between the veins, with the veins of the leaves remaining green. Leaves may start to drop if it is severe. Chlorosis (yellowing) is generally caused by a high pH rather than a lack of iron. To remedy, correct pH. If necessary, foliar feed with fertilizer containing soluble chelated iron.

Other micronutrients - manganese, boron, molybdenum, zinc and copper - are rarely deficient in any soil. By using commercial potting soil, fortified soilless mix, or N-P-K fertilizer with trace elements, you are guaranteed that all necessary trace elements are available. Fertilizers that contain only trace elements are available, but may be very tricky to use. Trace elements are necessary in minute amounts and reach toxic levels easily. Do not use a chemical trace element fertilizer more than once every two months or unless it is absolutely necessary. Liquid seaweed is the safest trace element formula to apply. Seaweed is natural, soluble and difficult to over apply.

Chapter Five

Hydroponic Gardening

The roots of hydroponics come from two Greek words that were put together: *hydro* meaning "water" and *ponos* meaning "labor." Today hydroponics is the science of growing plants without soil, most often in a soilless mix. With hydroponics, two very important factors may be totally controlled: nutrient intake and oxygen intake via roots.

Hydroponic gardening, like HID gardening, is easy and fun, once the concept and principles are understood. There are a few basic rules that must be followed to make a good system productive. First, let's look at how and why hydroponics works.

In hydroponics, the inert soilless medium contains essentially no nutrients of its own. All the nutrients are supplied by the nutrient solution (technically this is aeroponics). This solution passes over the roots or floods around them at regular intervals, later draining off. The oxygen around the roots is able to speed the plants' uptake of nutrients. Plants grow faster hydroponically because they are able to assimilate nutrients faster. They are able to take in food as fast as they are able to utilize it. In soil, as in hydroponics, the roots absorb nutrients and water; even the best soil rarely contains as much oxygen as a soilless hydroponic medium.

Hydroponics works well for horticulturists who are willing to spend a few extra minutes a day in their garden.

The garden requires extra maintenance; plants grow faster, there are more things to check.

In fact, some people do not like hydroponic gardening, because it requires too much additional care.

All too often, people who just started indoor gardening get so excited about it that they go too far too fast. They buy new little garden gadgets and have many more projects going than they can properly manage. The biggest problem some people have in purchasing hydroponic systems, is following the directions to assemble the system. This is important to remember when thinking about constructing and inventing your own unit. It will take a month or two to work out most of the bugs in a homemade unit.

Hydroponic gardening is exacting and not as forgiving as soil gardening. The soil works as a buffer for nutrients and holds them longer than the inert medium of hydroponics. In fact, some very advanced hydroponic systems do not even use a soilless mix. The roots are suspended in the air and misted with nutrient solution. The misting chamber is kept dark so algae do not compete with roots. This form of hydroponics is called aeroponics.

Plants, properly maintained, grown hydroponically under HID lamps tend to grow a little more lush foliage and at a faster rate than plants grown in soil. The garden calendar is usually moved up one or two weeks. The real benefit with hydroponics is realized later in the plant's life. When roots are restricted and growth slows in containerized plants, hydroponically grown plants are still getting the maximum amount of nutrients.

This easy to operate garden by American Hydroponics simplifies growing.

The wick system of hydroponic gardening cuts watering frequency. Simply fill the lower reservoir with a mild fertilizer solution.

The principles involved in hydroponics are simple and direct, but the application of these principles can become very complex. Gravel is the inert medium most commonly used to hold the roots and stabilize the plant while the nutrient solution passes over the roots in one of many ways. The nutrient solution drains away from the roots, so the oxygen will have a chance to work with the roots to draw in the nutrients. These are the basic principles of hydroponics. The nutrient solution, its application, and the growing medium are the main variables.

Different Systems

The way the nutrient solution is applied distinguishes the various systems. Hydroponic systems may be classified as active or passive. An active system actively moves the nutrient solution. Examples of active systems are: fill and drain, and top feed.

Passive systems rely on the capillary action of the wick and the growing medium. The nutrient solution is passively absorbed by the wick, medium and roots. The mediums that are normally used in a wick system are vermiculite, sawdust, peat moss etc. For rapid growth, the average wick system keeps the medium too wet; consequently, not enough air is available to the roots.. However, the wick system works very well if engineered properly. The soilless medium, the number of wicks, their gauge and texture are the main variables involved in a wick system.

The wick system has no moving parts. There is nothing mechanical to break, replace or malfunction. Wick systems also boast a low initial cost. Once set up and functioning properly, they require little work to maintain. Wick systems are perfect for slow-growing perennials such as African violets and rex begonias.

Hydroponic systems are further classified as recovery and non-recovery. Non-recovery means just what it says. Once the nutrient solution is applied to the inert growing medium, it is not recovered. These systems use sand, gravel, sawdust, expanded clay, or rockwool as the medium. No nutrient solution is recovered; less is applied, promoting less waste, complication and labor. Non-recovery systems are used mainly for commercial applications where the soilless medium is plentiful and the soil is not arable.

The flood and top feed methods are active recovery systems. They actively work by moving a volume of nutrient solution into contact with the roots. Recovery, because the nutrient solution is recovered after it has drained off and will be used again. These systems tend to use mediums that will drain fairly rapidly and hold lots of air, such as pea gravel, light pumice rock or crushed brick. The flood method is used many commercial hydroponic operations and many home systems. The Hydrofarm™ is a (bottom) flood system. This system has proved to be low-maintenance and easy to use.

The top feed method is a little more intricate, but used in hydroponic units with excellent results. There are many very efficient top feed systems. The nutrient solution is delivered by a hose overhead. See drawing, page 62.

In a flood system, the water floods into the bed, usually from the bottom, pushing the CO_2-rich, oxygen-poor air out. When the medium drains, it draws the new oxygen-rich air into the growing medium. Top feed systems apply the nutrient solution to the base of each plant with a small hose. The solution is aerated as it flows through the air.

NFT (Nutrient Film Technique) hydroponic systems are the most productive available. They operate on a very simple principle. The roots grow into a shallow mat located in a light-tight draining grow bed. Nutrient solution flows over the roots up to 24 hours per day. The majority of the roots actually grow on top of the thin matting. The nutrient solution flows slowly over the roots. This system allows the most air and nutrients to be absorbed by the roots. Growth is unbelievable in a fine tuned NFT hydroponic system.

Emily's all purpose garden by *Hydrofarm*™

Low maintenance and operating cost, simplicity and abundant yields characterize Higher Yield's medialess Buddy System.

(A) Tubs for reservoir and growth chamber - table support
(B) Typical system set-up
(C) Multiple set-up

Flood & Drain Gardens

HYDRO-KITS

Solution

NFT Systems

This wick system garden is nearly maintenance free. The containers can be removed in this simple wick system garden.

The Growing Medium

The purpose of the growing medium is to harbor oxygen, water, and nutrients, and support the root system of a plant. As with soil, the texture of the soilless medium is of utmost importance. The texture should be one that lets the solution drain rapidly enough for the roots to get a good supply of oxygen. A fast-draining medium, holding little water for a long time, is ideal for active recovery hydroponic systems.

Fibrous materials, such as vermiculite, hold much moisture within their cells. This type of medium is desired with a passive, capillary action, wick system.

The size of the medium is important. The smaller the particles, the closer they pack and the slower they drain. The larger the particles, the faster they drain and the more air they hold.

Irregular materials have more surface area and hold more water than round ones, which hold less water. Avoid gravel with sharp edges that could cut a plant's roots if it fell or was jostled around. Round pea gravel, smooth, washed gravel, crushed brick, or some form of lava are the best mediums for growing flowers and vegetables in an active recovery system. Rock should be of igneous (volcanic) origin. This type of rock tends to have a neutral pH and will not break down under hydroponic growing conditions. Gravel is the most widely used hydroponic growing medium for flowers and vegetables. It holds moisture and nutrients without staying too wet. The best gravel to use for growing indoors is a pea gravel that is one-eighth- to three-eights-inch in diameter. Ideally, over half of the medium should be about a quarter-inch in diameter.

Hydrofarm supplies a ceramic hydroponic medium called *Geolite* that could be better than gravel. In any case, wash gravel and ceramic rock thoroughly to get out all the dust, which turns to sediment.

The medium should be clean so as not to react to nutrients. For example, gravel from a limestone quarry is packed with calcium carbonate and old concrete is full of lime. When mixed with water, calcium carbonate will raise the pH. The concrete is toxic to plants. Other mixtures made from pebbles or anything near the ocean could be full of ocean salt. If you suspect the medium is toxic, it may be easier to get another load of medium than to try to flush away the salts.

Rockwool

Rockwool is the neatest invention since the sun! It is an inert, sterile, porous, non-degradable growing medium that provides firm root support. Like all soilless mediums, rockwool acts as a temporary reservoir for nutrients. This affords the grower a tremendous amount of control over plant growth through nutrient uptake.

This revolutionary new growing medium consists of thin strand-like fibers made primarily from limestone, granite or almost any kind of rock. With the appearance of lent collected by a cloths dryer, rockwool does not resemble any other growing media.

Rockwool has been used for many years as home and industrial insulation. In fact, the walls in your home may be packed full of rockwool. The rockwool used for insulation is similar to the horticultural grade.

Rockwool holds up to 20% air even when it is saturated with nutrient solution.

Rockwool is the growing medium of choice in Holland. This entire greenhouse is watered automatically.

nutrients that are not used will simply drain off. A fresh nutrient-rich solution is used for the next watering.

Enough nutrient solution is applied to get a 10 to 20 percent drain or leaching effect. Leaching flushes out excess salts from the medium and applies adequate nutrient solution to the medium.

Rockwool slabs contain pepper plants in neat rows.

Definite advantages are reaped when growing in this soilless substrate. It is economical, consistent and easy to control. *Best of all, rockwool's fibrous structure and will hold up to 20 percent air even when it is completely saturated.*

Rockwool was introduced into the U.S. in 1985. The word travels slowly and the American horticultural community has been slow to adapt. Most gardeners have not even heard of rockwool.

Rockwool has been used in European greenhouses for over 15 years. It was first discovered in Denmark in 1969. Growers began using rockwool as a way around the ban on soil-grown nursery stock imposed by some of the European community. Today, an estimated 50 percent of all Western European greenhouse vegetables are grown exclusively in rockwool.

Other mediums like peat and soils are becoming more expensive to produce and can easily vary in quality. This fact, coupled with the high cost of sterilization, prompted European growers to explore new alternatives.

Rockwool can be used in both recovery and non-recovery hydroponic systems. As explained earlier, the nutrient solution in a recovery system is constantly changing. Salts soon build up to toxic levels as plants use selected nutrients in the solution. The nutrient solution must be monitored constantly and adjusted to provide the exact concentration of nutrients for optimum growth. However, with a non-recovery system, the excess nutrient solution drains off and is not recovered. The plants get all the nutrients they need and any

European growers switched to rockwool because it is inexpensive and easy to control. They not only changed, growers continued to use it.

Rockwool is produced from rock alone or a combination of rock, limestone and coke. The rigid components are melted at temperatures exceeding 2,500 F. This molten solution is poured over a spinning cylinder, very similar to the way cotton candy is made with liquified sugar. As the molten solution flies off the cylinder, it elongates and cools to form fibers. These fibers could be likened to cotton candy fibers. The product of these fibers, rockwool, is then pressed into uniform blocks, sheets, cubes or granulated. The blocks are rigid and easy to handle. They can be cut into just about any size desirable. Granulated rockwool is easily placed into growing containers or used like vermiculite and perlite as a soil amendment.

When used with an open ended drip system, rockwool is easily irrigated with a nutrient solution controlled by a timer. The usual procedure in Europe is to apply a small amount of fertilizer two or three times a day. Enough excess solution is applied to obtain a 10-25 percent leeching effect every day.

> **Note:** *Gardening: The Rockwool Book* is available at many garden centers from order blank in the back of this book. It is the best book on growing with rockwool for the home gardener.

To transplant seedlings grown in rockwool cubes, simply set the one-inch cube in a pre-drilled hole in the larger cube. The roots branch out into the slab quickly.

A plastic covering prevents the growth of algae on rockwool slabs. The convenient square shape makes the slabs easy to stack and use for individual plants.

Do not let all of this control fool you. Even though rockwool will hold 10-14 times as much water as soil, it does not provide the buffering action available in soil. The pH of rockwool is about 7.8. An acidic fertilizer solution (about 5.5 on the pH scale) is required to maintain the actual solution at a pH of about 6.5 or lower. Errors made in the nutrient solution mix or with pH level, will be magnified. Be careful to monitor both the pH and nutrient level with a watchful eye.

There are some tricks to handling rockwool. Dry rockwool can be abrasive and act as an irritant to the skin. When handling dry rockwool, use gloves and goggles. Once the rockwool is thoroughly wet, it is easy and safe to work with; it creates no dust and does not irritate to the skin. Keep out of the reach of children and wash clothes thoroughly after prolonged use around rockwool as a safety precaution.

Rockwool stays so wet that algae grows on surfaces exposed to light. While this green slimy algae is unsightly, it does not compete with plants for nutrition. However, harmless fungus gnats could take up residence. Avoid the unsightly algae by covering the rockwool with plastic.

Sterilizing

The medium must be sterilized before each new planting. Sterilizing is much easier than replacing the medium. For apartment dwellers, hydroponics provides an alternative to heavy, messy soil gardening. Instead of toting copious quantities of soil in and out of the building, the soilless medium is simply sterilized and reused. Soil can become expensive. The reason for sterilization is to prevent any bad micro-organisms from getting started in the garden.

Before sterilizing, the roots will have to be removed from the medium. An average tomato plant (four or five feet tall, three or four months old) will have a root mass about the size of a desk telephone. Roots can create a huge mass in larger bed systems. A few roots can remain in the system, but try to get at least 90 to 95 percent of them out. The system has less of a chance of clogging if few roots remain. A clogged system does not fill or drain properly.

The roots will tend to mat up near the bottom of the bed. It is easiest to remove them in one large mat. Some of the medium may be embedded in the roots. It is easier to get more medium than trying to pick it from between the roots.

There are many ways to sterilize the medium. The method used to sterilize most systems is very easy. First, remove the nutrient solution from the tank. Then, make up a solution of ordinary laundry bleach such as Clorox or Purex (calcium or sodium hypochlorite) or hydrochloric acid, the kind used in hot tubs and swimming pools.

Apply one cup of bleachper five gallons of water, flood the medium with the sterilizing solution for at least one half-hour, then flush. Use lots of fresh water to leach and flush the entire system: beds, connecting hoses and drains. Make sure all the toxic chemicals are gone by flushing the entire system for at least one hour (two intervals of half an hour each) before replanting.

The Hydroponic Nutrient Solution

To gain a more complete background on ,nutrients etc., read Chapter Four, "Water and Fertilizer." The same basic principles that apply to soil also apply to the hydroponic medium.

Always use the best fertilizer you can find. The fertilizers recommended in this book have worked well for hydroponic gardening. Ecogrow, Dyna Gro, Hydrolife, Green Leaves, General Hydroponics, Dutch Magic and Formula One are popular because of their complete formulas. Hydroponic fertilizers should have *all* of the necessary macro- and micronutrients.

Like soil, hydroponic gardens can be fertilized organically or chemicals. An organic hydroponic garden is more work to maintain than one using prepared chemical fertilizers.

Organic teas must be prepared in a tea bag to ensure that the pipes do not plug with residue and sludge. Cheap fertilizer (not recommended), like organic fertilizers, contains sludge, which could build up and require more frequent cleaning of the system.

Fertilizers should be chelated, to help nutrient uptake by roots. Chelated nutrientsare soluble and immediately available to the plant.

For fast-growing annuals, the nutrient solution should be changed at least every two (at the most three) weeks. It can go longer, but growth could slow and deficiencies result. Changing the solution as often as every week would not hurt anything. Plants absorb nutrientsat different rates, and some of the elements are depleted before others. The best form of preventive maintenance is to change the solution often. Fertilizer is probably the least expensive necessity in a garden. If you skimp on fertilizer or try to save it, the garden may be stunted so badly it will not recover in time to produce a good crop. The pH is also continually changing,

due to its reaction to the nutrient uptake. This is another reason to change the nutrient solution frequently. The nutrientsbeing used at different rates could create a salt (unused fertilizer) buildup. This problem is usually averted by using pure nutrientsand flushing the soilless medium thoroughly with fresh, tepid water between nutrient solutions.

Its easy to maintain plants in this simple flood and drain garden from Hydrofarm.

 RULE OF THUMB: Change the nutrient solution every two weeks.

Hydroponics gives the means to supply the maximum nutrientsa plant needs. It can also starve them to death or over-feed them rapidly. Remember most hydroponic systems are designed for high-performance system. If one thing malfunctions, - the electricity goes off, the pump breaks, the drain gets clogged with roots, or there is a rapid fluctuation in the pH - it could cause severe problems with the garden. A mistake could kill or stunt plants so badly that they never fully recover.

Always use a *complete* hydroponic fertilizer.

PH

Most flowers and vegetables grow hydroponically within a pH range of 5.8 to 6.8, 6.3 is ideal. The pH in hydroponic gardens requires an extremely vigilant eye by the gardener. All of the nutrients are in solution. The pH of the nutrient solution changes easily. The roots use nutrients at different rates. The changes in the amounts of nutrients in the solution will the pH. If the pH is not within the acceptable hydroponic range (6 to 6.5), nutrients may not be absorbed as fast as possible.

 RULE OF THUMB: Check the pH every day or two to make sure it is at or near the perfect level.

Do not use sodium hydroxide to raise pH. It is very caustic and difficult to handle. Potassium hydroxide is much easier to use.

This innovative hydroponic garden is totally self contained and mobile.

The Reservoir

The reservoir should be as large as possible. Be prepared! Forgetting to replenish the nutrient solution could easily result in crop failure! Plants use much more water than nutrients. Water also evaporates from the system. An approximate water loss of 5 to 25 percent per day, depending on climatic conditions and the size of plants, can be expected. This amounts to many, many gallons of solution per week. Less evaporation occurs when there is a top on the reservoir. When water is used, the concentration of elements in the solution increases; there is less water in the solution and nearly the same amount of nutrients. More sophisticated systems have a float valve that adds more water as it is used from the reservoir. Most systems have a full line on the inside of the reservoir tank to show when the solution is low. Water should be added as soon as the solution level lowers, which could be as often as every day! The reservoir should contain at least 20 percent more nutrient solution than it takes to fill the beds, to compensate for evaporation. The larger the volume of nutrient solution, the more buffering capacity, and the easier it is to control.

 RULE OF THUMB: Check the level of the reservoir daily and replenish if necessary.

It is a big job to empty and refill a hydroponic reservoir with 20 to 60 gallons of water. To make the task easier, the system should be able to pump the solution out of the reservoir. If the water must sit for a couple of days to let chlorine dissipate or to alter the pH before putting it into the tank, the system should pump water back into the reservoir. Using the pump in the reservoir to move nutrient solution will greatly ease your task as a hydroponic horticulturist. If you are unable to pump the used nutrient solution out of the reservoir, place the unit at such an altitude that it may be siphoned or flow by gravity into a drain or outdoor garden.

The used nutrient solution can pumped into the vegetable garden outdoors, or down the nearest drain. Do not dump the nutrient solution into a septic tank. The fertilizer disrupts the chemical balance of a septic tank, causing it to overflow. Do not use this unbalanced nutrient solution on other indoor plants.

Check the catalog in the back of this book for more books about hydroponics.

The Irrigation Cycle

The irrigation or watering cycle depends on the same things as does the soil: plant size, climatic conditions and the type of growing medium. If the particles are large, round and smooth, and drain rapidly like pea gravel, the cycle will be often: two to four times daily.

Flood systems with pea gravel are generally flooded two or three times daily for 15 to 30 minutes. The water rises to within half an inch of the top of the gravel and should completely drain out of the medium at each watering. Top feed systems are usually cycled for about 30 minutes and should be watered two to four times daily.

During and soon after irrigation, the nutrient content of the bed and the reservoir are at the same concentration. As time passes between irrigation cycles, the nutrient concentration and the pH gradually change. If enough time passes between watering, the nutrient concentration may change so much that the plant is not able to absorb nutrients properly.

There are many irrigation regimens. As with soil, experimentation will probably tell you more than anything else. One gardener explained to me, "After a while you kind of get the feel for it." It took this hydroponic horticulturist nearly a year to master the irrigation cycle. If possible, try experiments on one or two plants at a time, instead of subjecting an entire bed or garden to an irrigation experiment.

The temperature of the nutrient solution should stay somewhere in the range of 65 to 75^0 F (18 to 24^0 C). If there is a problem with keeping the room warm in winter, the nutrient solution can be heated instead of the room. Submerge a grounded aquarium heater or grounded heat cables to heat the nutrient solution. It may take a few days for the cables or heater to heat a large volume of solution. Never place the heat cable in the soilless hydroponic medium. The heat from the cable could fry the roots when the medium dries out.

When air is cooler than water, the water evaporates into the air rapidly. The greater the temperature differential, the more humid the air. For more information, see "Relative Humidity", pages 93-94.

The nutrient solution should be replaced with water that is at least 60^0 F (15^0 C). Cold water shocks plants. The new water could take a few days to warm up, meanwhile all the plants could get stunted!

Never let the water temperature get higher than 85^0 F (29^0 C). If roots get too hot, they could be damaged. Submersible heaters of any kind must be grounded and constructed of materials (usually plastic) that give off no harmful residues. Aquarium heaters are safe and very popular.

Hydroponic Nutrient Disorders

When the hydroponic garden is on a regular maintenance schedule, nutrient problems are usually averted. Change the nutrient solution if you do not know the cause of the nutrient disorder. This method is the easiest and the most secure. If you can determine the exact cause of the disorder, add 10 to 20 percent more of the deficient ingredient for two weeks or until the disorder has disappeared.

Read "Nutrient Disorders," pages 74-76. Hydroponic gardens must be watched more closely than a soil garden. If an unstable pH causes a nutrient deficiency, novice gardeners may not notice the problem until it is in its advanced stages. Treatment must be rapid and certain, but it will take a few days for the plant to respond to the remedies. Foliar feed the sick plants for fast results. What if two or more elements are deficient at the same time? This may give plants the appearance of having no specific cause, just symptoms! When this sort of mind-bending problem occurs, change the nutrient solution immediately! Fresh nutrient solution supplies the missing elements. The plants do not have to be diagnosed, just treated.

 RULE OF THUMB: If the garden has a nutrient disorder, change the nutrient solution and adjust the pH.

Over-fertilization (page 75), once diagnosed, is easy to treat. Drain the nutrient solution, then flush with fresh, tepid water. The number of times the system is flushed depends on the severity of the problem. Flush at least twice. Replace with properly mixed solution.

Nutrient disorders will occur to all the plants at the same time if they are receiving the same solution. Climatic disorders - windburn, lack of light, temperature stress, fungi and insect damage - usually show up on the plants that are most affected. For example, plants that are next to a heat vent may show signs of heat scorch, while the rest of the garden looks healthy. Or a plant on the edge of the garden may be small or leggy, since it receives less light.

Building Your Own Hydroponic System

One option is to build your own hydroponic system. This is easy, but there are certain things that must be looked after for the system to work properly. Sealing all joints and using few or no seams are two basic codes of hydroponic garden construction. Seal seams with waterproof caulk or use fiberglass resin and material to ensure no-leak construction. Imagine how you would feel if you returned from a short vacation to find the hydroponic system flooded the upstairs bedroom the afternoon you left. Drain holes or pipe connections must fit snugly, with no leakage. Teflon tape is a good anti-leak companion for threaded connections.

Many hydroponic systems using the fill-and-drain method must have elevated beds so the solution drains back into the reservoir. Consider the added elevation when building and installing hydroponic units in rooms with limited ceiling space. The reservoir can be placed in a hole in the floor if ceiling space is limit.

A large, covered reservoir is very convenient. The larger the container, the more solution and the more forgiving. The more solution available, the longer it takes to become depleted; the pH will fluctuate less and it will generally be more stable.

The size of the hydroponic container is important. The roots have to grow big enough to support a plant. In large bed systems, the roots form a large mat of tangled roots. In smaller one to three gallon beds, roots could fill the container and grow out the bottom in two to six weeks. As with soil, the size of the hydroponic container dictates its buffering capacity.

Roots may clog the drain. Place a small mesh screen (quarter-inch or less) made from a non-corrosive material, such as plastic, over the drain. The screen should be easy to remove and clean.

The frequency of watering depends on the soilless medium used. A fast-draining medium such as pea gravel, requires watering two to four times daily. Slow-draining vermiculite requires irrigation only once a day or less. Fill the bed so it is evenly moist; drain it completely and rapidly so oxygen will be available to roots as soon as possible.

A simple flood system can be fabricated from a five-gallon plastic bucket, filled with washed gravel, that has a drain hole in the bottom. The hole is plugged with a cork. The nutrient solution, kept in another five-gallon bucket, is poured into the bed. After 20 to 30 minutes, the cork is removed, and the nutrient solution drains back into the reservoir/bucket. This method is a little sloppy since the liquid is poured through the air (which also aerates it). This system provides an easy, inexpensive way for soil gardeners to get their hands wet with hydroponic gardening.

Another manual, gravity-flow system has a reservoir/bucket attached to a bed bucket with a flexible hose. The reservoir/bucket is raised above the bed so that the nutrient solution flows into it. After 15-30 minutes, the reservoir/bucket is lowered to let the solution flow back into it. This simple system could take a couple of hours to set up, and may require a trip to the hardware store for some plastic fittings. Once set up, the system creates no mess and no fuss. Just be there daily to lift and lower the reservoir/bucket. Remember to pay close attention to the evaporation of the nutrient solution!

A basic hydroponic system is manufactured with a simple hose and a movable bucket.

This hydroponic system moves the nutrient solution with a submergible pump (outlined).

The next kind of active, recovery hydroponic system employs an aquarium pump and works on the bottom flood method. Air is pumped into a sealed container full of nutrient solution. The pressure created by the pump forces the solution into the hydroponic bed. The pump actually pumps air into the nutrient solution! After the solution is in the bed, the pump continues forcing air through the solution. It aerates the nutrient solution while it is in contact with the roots. This system is easily automated. An inexpensive timer can be attached to the pump so the system will operate automatically, keeping the solution in the bed for up to an hour. This system works great for people who will not be there every day to cycle the nutrients manually.

Note: Be careful to keep the pump from running dry.

Another active, recovery, flood system uses a submergible pump, which is a little more expensive. This type of system is able to recycle the nutrients several times daily at 20- to 30-minute cycles. This is the system many home gardeners and professionals use. It is one of the most successful, because of its ease of operation and the control that may be exercised. The nutrient solution is cycled several times per day; maximum nutrient application and uptake are achieved. A timer can be attached to the pump, which automates the system. The pump should stay submerged to prevent air lock.

Getting Started

Starting seeds in the medium may not be very easy. Tiny seeds easily wash away, get too deep or dry out in coarse mediums. Many people prefer to plant seeds or cuttings in a peat pot or rockwool cube. The pot or cube is transplanted into the medium after the plant is two or three weeks old. Cuttings transplant best into a hydroponic garden using a rockwool cube or peat pot. When cuttings are placed into the hydroponic medium, the rockwool cube will be able to hold the extra moisture it needs for the dry times between irrigation cycles.

Read "Transplanting," pages 127. Transplanting is easy in hydroponics. Simply remove the plant from the medium, and place it in another place in the medium. The younger the plant the better transplanting works. If the roots are allowed to grow too long, they will break when moved in transplanting. Shock will result if the roots are broken off and not gently returned to the medium. After transplanting, scoop up some of the nutrient solution or mix a B_1 solution and pour it over the newly moved transplant. Then, cycle the nutrient solution through the system so it gets adequate moisture to let roots settle in.

It is okay to water a bed four to six times per day if necessary. Make sure the nutrient solution drains completely out after each irrigation. The maximum watering cycle should be no longer than 30 minutes.

An external pump transfers the nutrient solution from the growing bed to the nutrient solution reservoir.

Chapter Six

Air

Fresh air is at the heart of all successful indoor gardens. Think about your role as Mother Nature. In the great outdoors, air is abundant and almost always fresh. The level of CO_2 in the air over a field of rapidly growing vegetation could be only one-third of normal on a very still day. Soon the wind blows in fresh new air. Rains cleanse the air and plants of dust and pollutants. The ecosystem of the great outdoors is always in motion. When plants are growing in a small room, Mother Nature really has to be on her toes to replicate the air of the great outdoors. Since there are none of the natural elements to make CO_2-rich, fresh air, you, Mother Nature, must take on the task!

Air is also used by the roots. Oxygen must be present along with water and nutrients for the roots to feed properly. If the soil is compacted or water-saturated, the roots have no air, and suffocate.

Fresh air is still easy to find and inexpensive to maintain. An exhaust fan is the main tool used to maintain fresh air.

Air provides essential elements for plant growth. A plant uses carbon dioxide (CO_2) and oxygen (O_2) from the air. Oxygen is used for respiration, burning carbohydrates and other foods, which produces energy. Carbon dioxide must be present during photosynthesis. Without CO_2 a plant will die! CO_2 uses light energy to combine with water, producing sugar. These sugars are used to fuel the growth and metabolism of the plant. Reduced levels of CO_2, slows growth to a crawl. Oxygen is given off as a by-product of this process. A plant will release more O_2 than is used and use much more CO_2 than it releases, except during darkness, when more oxygen is used.

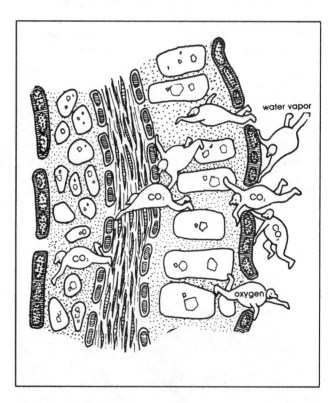

Close up of the stomata shows the exchange of oxygen and CO_2.

Plants and animals (remember people are animals too) complement one another. Plants give off oxygen as a by-product, making it available to people. People give off CO_2 as a by-product, making it available to plants. Without plants, animals could not live, and without animals, plants could not live as we know life today. Animals inhale air, using CO_2 to carry on life processes, and exhale CO_2 as a by-product.

Air Movement

In order to have a good flow of air through the stomata, adequate air circulation and ventilation are necessary. Indoors, fresh air is one of the most commonly overlooked factors contributing to a bountiful harvest. Fresh air is the least expensive element that can be made available to a plant. Experienced gardeners really understand the importance of fresh air, and take the time to set up a vent fan. Three factors affect air movement: stomata, ventilation, and circulation.

Stomata are microscopic pores on the leaf's underside, similar to an animal's nostrils. Animals regulate the amount of O_2 inhaled and CO_2 exhaled through the nostrils via the lungs. In a plant, O_2 and CO_2 flows are regulated by the stomata. The larger the plant, the more stomata it has to take in CO_2 and release CO_2. The greater the volume of plants, the more CO_2-rich air they need to keep them growing fast. Dirty, clogged stomata restrict the air flow. Stomata are easily clogged by dirt, polluted air or sprays that leave a filmy residue. Dirty, clogged stomata are sealed off and unable to function. In nature, stomata are cleaned by rain and wind. Indoors, the horticulturist must make rain with a sprayer and wind with a fan.

Vent fan is easily set in lower half of open window.

 RULE OF THUMB: Plants should be washed with clean, tepid water on both sides of the leaves at least once a month. See: "About Spraying," pages 116-118.

Circulation - If the air is totally still, plants tend to use all of the CO_2 next to the leaf. When this air is used and no new CO_2-rich air is forced into its place, a dead air space forms around the leaf, stifling the stomata, slowing growth. Air also tends to stratify. The warm air stays near the ceiling and cooler air, close to the floor. All of these potential problems are avoided by opening a door or window and installing an oscillating ceiling fan. Air circulation is also important for insect and fungus prevention. Mold spores are present in all rooms. Spores are kept from landing and growing when the air is stirred up by a fan.

An oscillating circulation fan will keep the air from stratifying in the grow room.

Ventilation - An average 10-by-10-foot vegetable garden will use from 10 to 30 gallons of water per week. Where does all that water go? It transpires and evaporates into the air. Therefore, gallons of water will be held in the air every week. If this moisture is left in a small room, the leaves will get limp, transpiration will slow and the stomata will be stifled. This moisture must be replaced with dry air that lets the stomata function properly. A vent fan that *pulls* air out of the grow room will do the trick!

Successful indoor gardeners know that a vent fan is as important as water, light, heat and fertilizer. In some cases fresh air is even more important. All greenhouses have large ventilation fans. Grow rooms are very similar to greenhouses, and their example should be followed. In most grow rooms there is a window or some easy-to-use opening in which to mount a fan. If no vent opening is available, one will have to be made.

Many different vent fans and timers are available to the indoor grower.

When installing a vent fan, allow an adequate exchange of air, but prevent cold backdrafts.

Use a dryer vent opening with a flap to prevent backdrafts. Use a four-inch flexible dryer hose for smaller grow rooms and eight-inch galvanized heat duct pipe for large installations. Place one end of the hose outdoors. One of the best vents is the chimney. The other end of the hose is attached to the vent fan. The vent fan is placed near the ceiling so that hot, humid air is vented. Check for leaks. Set up the fan. See: "Setting Up the Vent Fan," pages 100-101.

Greenhouse fans are equipped with baffles or flaps to prevent backdrafts. In cold or hot weather backdrafts could change the room temperature, stifle growth and encourage a menagerie of bad bugs and fungi. Vent flaps avoid this problem.

Vent fans are rated by the number of cubic feet of air per minute (CFM) they can replace or move. Buy a fan that will replace the volume (cubic feet) of the grow room in about five minutes. The air pulled out is immediately replaced by fresh air that is drawn in through the numerous tiny cracks or openings in the room. If the grow room is sealed tightly to control moisture, an open window or air intake vent may be necessary to allow for enough inflow of new air.

Why use a vent fan? The reason is simple: efficiency. A vent fan is able to *pull* air out of a room many times more efficiently than a fan is able to *push* it out. A fan in the middle of a room that pushes the air out of a room is up against a tough physical principle. It is all a matter of pressure. The fan pushes air, increasing the air pressure in the room. This pressure must increase substantially in order for a rapid exchange of air to take place. The vent fan, on the other hand, is able to change the pressure rapidly. It is much easier to lower the air pressure, causing new fresh air to rush in to fill the vacuum.

A maximum/minimum thermometer will measure the present temperature and tell you how cold it was last night.

Temperature

Every grow room should be equipped with an accurate thermometer to measure the temperature. The mercury or liquid type is usually more accurate than the spring or dial models. Thermometers are inexpensive and they supply important information. Make sure to get one. The ideal thermometer is a day-night or maximum-minimum type. Using this thermometer, the horticulturist is able to see how low the temperature drops at night and how high it reaches during the day. This is very important for many reasons that are explained below.

Under normal conditions, the ideal temperature range for indoor plant growth is 72 to 76^0 F (22 to 24^0 C).

At night, the temperature can usually drop 10 to 15^0 (1 to 2^0 C) with no noticeable effect on growth rate. The temperature should not drop more than

20^0 F (10^0 C), or excessive humidity and mold may become a problem. Daytime temperatures over 100^0 F (38^0 C) and below 60^0 F (15^0 C) seem to slow down growth in most plants. Maintaining the proper, constant temperature in the grow room promotes strong, even, healthy growth. Make sure plants are not too close to a heat source, such as a ballast or heat vent. It could dry them out, maybe even cause heat scorch!

Temperatures above 90^0 F (32^0 C) are not recommended. Increased temperatures speed chemical activity, causing excessive stress if ventilation is not increased. As explained in the following section on humidity, the greater the temperature, the more water the air is able to hold. This moist air stifles the stomata and slows rather than speeds growth. Other problems could result from the excess moisture, including: fungi and moisture condensation when the temperature drops at night.

Heat buildup indoors can become a problem in warm and hot weather. The ideal grow room is located underground, in a basement, with the insulating qualities of the earth. With the added heat of the HID, and 100^0 (38^0 C) temperatures outdoors, a room can heat up really fast. Several gardeners have lost their gardens to heatstroke during the Fourth of July weekend. This is the first big summer holiday and everybody in the city wants to get away to enjoy it. There are always some gardeners who forget to maintain good ventilation in the grow room while on vacation. In a room that is improperly set up, with no vent fan and no insulating walls, the summer temperatures may climb to 120^0 (48^0 C). There is no way a plant can live in this climate without incredible amounts of water and ventilation. Mother Nature would never let her climate change to this lethal level, would you?

The cold of winter is the other extreme. Several years ago, the Oregon winter was colder than normal. In Portland, electricity went out, heat went off and pipes froze. Residents were driven from their homes until the electricity was restored a few days later. Several gardeners returned and found their lovely garden wilted, with the deepest, most disgusting green only a freeze can bring. Broken pipes were spewing water everywhere. It is very important to keep the grow room above 35^0 F (2^0 C). If it drops far below 35^0 F (2^0 C), the freeze will destroy the cells of warm-weather plants, and foliage will die or not be able to grow very fast. Growth generally slows when the temperature is below 50^0 F (10^0 C), so try to keep the grow room warm.

A thermostat regulates the temperature in a room. It measures the temperature, then turns a heat or a cooling source on or off to keep the temperature stays within a specified range. A thermostat may be attached to an electric or combustion heater. In fact, many homes are already set up with electric baseboard heat and have a thermostat in each room.

Thermostats are for either heating or cooling. A heating thermostat turns on a heater when the temperature *drops below* a trigger point. A cooling thermostat turns a fan or cooler on when the temperature *climbs beyond* a trigger point. The thermostat is attached to a vent fan in all but the coldest grow rooms. When it gets too hot, the thermostat turns the vent fan on, forcing the hot, stale air out of the room. The vent fan runs until the desired temperature is reached, then the thermostat turns the fan off. The vent fan should be all the temperature control necessary. A refrigerated air conditioner can be installed if heat and humidity are a big problem. If excessive heat is a problem, but humidity is not a concern, an evaporative swamp cooler is the best value.

Thermostats are either single-stage or two-stage. The single-stage costs $20 to $30 and is able to keep the temperature the same both day and night. The two-stage thermostat is more expensive, about $50, but can maintain different day and night temperatures. This is very convenient and can save you quite a bit of money, since the room temperature may drop 10 to 15^0 F (-12 to -9^0 C) at night with no effect on growth.

Uninsulated grow rooms and greenhouses experience broad changes in temperature. They require special considerations. First, it would probably be easiest to grow somewhere else, but if you have to use an attic or hot spot, allow lots of ventilation. Make sure to enclose the room so that heating and cooling are easier and less expensive.

When CO_2 is enriched to .12 to .15 percent, a temperature range from 75 to 85^0 F (24 to 30^0 C) promotes more rapid exchange of gases. Photosynthesis and chlorophyll synthesis are able to take place at a more rapid rate and plants grow faster. Remember, this extra 10 to 15^0 (6 to 9^0 C) increases water, nutrient and space consumption, so be prepared!

Seeds germinate faster and cuttings root quicker when the temperature range is from 75 to 85^0 F (24 to 30^0 C). Two easy ways to increase temperature when cloning are: using soil heating tape, and building a (plastic) tent to cover young germinating seeds or cuttings. A plastic tent increases both temperature and humidity. Remove the tent cover as soon as the seeds sprout above the soil, to allow for circulation. Cuttings, however, should remain covered throughout the entire rooting process. Always watch for signs of mold or rot when using a humidity tent with cuttings. Allowing a bit of air circulation and ventilating cuttings under the tent daily helps prevent fungus. An alternative to a humidity tent would be to mist the cuttings several times daily with a spray bottle.

The temperature in the grow room tends to stay the same, top to bottom, when the air is circulated with an oscillating fan. Normally, in an enclosed grow room, a 1000-watt HID lamp and ballast will provide enough heat. A remote ballast, placed on a shelf or a stand near the floor, also helps break up air stratification by radiating heat upward. Cooler climates have enough heat during the day when the outdoor temperature rises, but not enough when lower temperatures set in at night. The lamp is adjusted to be on during the cool nights. This will warm the room to an acceptable level both night and day.

Sometimes it is just too cold for the lamp and ballast to maintain adequate room temperatures. Many grow rooms are equipped with a central heating and air conditioning vent. This vent is usually controlled by a central thermostat that regulates the entire home's heat. By adjusting the thermostat to 72^0 F (22^0 C) and opening all the internal doors in the home, the grow room can stay a cozy 72^0 (22^0 C). For most gardeners, this is too expensive and very wasteful. Usually, keeping the thermostat between 60 and 65^0 (15 and 18^0 C), coupled with the heat from the HID system, is enough to sustain the desired temperature range. Other supplemental heat sources may work better than the above. Incandescent light bulbs and electric heaters are expensive, but provide instant heat. Incandescent bulbs even increase light intensity and add to the spectrum. Propane and natural gas heaters not only heat the air, but burn oxygen from the air, creating CO_2 as a by-product. This dual advantage makes their use even more economical.

There are several new kerosene heaters on the market today that work well for heating and CO_2 generation. Look for a heater that burns its fuel completely and leaves no telltale odor in the room. Watch out for old kerosene heaters or inefficient fuel oil heaters of any type. They could be dangerous! Diesel oil is a common type of indoor heat. Many furnaces use this dirty and polluting heat source. Wood heat is not the cleanest, but works well as a heat source. A vent fan is extremely important to bring new fresh air into a room heated by a polluting furnace.

Insect populations and fungi are also affected by temperature. Overall, the cooler it is, the slower the insects and fungus reproduce and develop. Temperature control is integrated into many insect and fungus control programs.

Relative humidity increases when the temperature drops at night. The more temperature variation, the greater the relative humidity variation. Supplemental heat or extra ventilation may be necessary at night if temperatures fluctuate more than 15^0 F (9^0 C).

 RULE OF THUMB: The moisture-holding capacity of air doubles with every 20^0 F (11^0 C) increase in temperature.

A 10-by-10-by-8-foot (800-cubic-foot) grow room can hold:

4 oz. of water at 32^0 F (0^0 C)
7 oz. of water at 50^0 F (10^0 C)
14 oz. of water at 70^0 F (22^0 C)
18 oz. of water at 80^0 F (27^0 C)
28 oz. of water at 90^0 F (32^0 C)
56 oz. of water at 100^0 F (38^0 C)

Humidity

Relative humidity is the ratio between the amount of moisture in the air and the greatest amount of moisture the air could hold at the same temperature. The hotter it is, the more moisture the air can hold; the cooler it is, the less moisture the air can hold. When the temperature in a grow room drops, the humidity climbs and moisture condenses. For example, a 1000-cubic foot (10-by-10-by-8-foot) room will hold a maximum of about 14 ounces of water when the temperature is 70^0 (21^0 C) and relative humidity is at 100 percent. When the temperature is increased to 100^0 (38^0 C)the same room will hold a whopping 56 ounces of moisture at 100 percent relative humidity. That's four times as much moisture! Where does this water go when the temperature drops?

Most vegetables grow best when the relative humidity range is from 40 to 60 percent. As with temperature, more or less constant humidity promotes healthy, even growth. Humidity affects the transpiration rate of the stomata. When high humidity exists, water evaporates slowly. The stomata close, transpiration slows, and so does plant growth. Water evaporates quickly into drier air-causing stomata to open, increasing transpiration and growth.

The proper relative humidity level is essential for healthy tropical and subtropical plants. Most flowering indoor plants require at least 50 percent relative humidity. Vegetables are just the opposite, they thrive in 50 percent or less, while indoor tropical gardens thrive in a relative humidity range of 65 to 70 percent.

Transpiration, the flow of water and CO_2 out of the leaf's stomata, in arid conditions will be rapid only if there is enough water available for roots. If water is inadequate, stomata will close to protect the plant from dehydration, causing growth to slow.

Relative humidity control is an integral part of insect and fungus prevention and control. High humidity (80 percent plus) promotes fungus and stem rot. Maintaining low (50 percent or less) humidity greatly reduces the chances of fungus formation. Some insect like humid conditions, others do not. Spider mites take much longer to reproduce in a humid room.

Relative humidity is measured with a hygrometer. This extremely important instrument could save you and your garden much frustration and fungus. If you know the exact moisture content in the air,   the humidity may be adjusted to a safe 50 percent level that encourages transpiration and discourages fungus growth.

There are two common types of hygrometers: the spring type, which is inexpensive (less than $10) and accurate to within 5 to 10 percent.   This hygrometer is just fine for most grow rooms, since the main concern is to keep the humidity near 50 percent. The other type of hygrometer, actually called a psychrometer, is a little more expensive (30 to 50) but is very accurate (See drawing below).   This   hygrometer (psychrometer) uses the wet and dry bulb principle. It is recommended if you are using several lamps and extreme accuracy is important.

A humidistat is similar to a thermostat, but it regulates humidity instead of temperature. Humidistats are wonderful!   They make playing Mother Nature a snap! Humidistats cost $30 to $50 and are worth their weight in flower blossoms. The more expensive models are the most accurate. The humidistat is wired in-line with the thermostat to the vent fan (See drawing on page 95). Each can operate the fan independently. As soon as the humidity (or temperature) gets out of the acceptable range, the fan turns on to vent the humid (or hot) air outdoors.

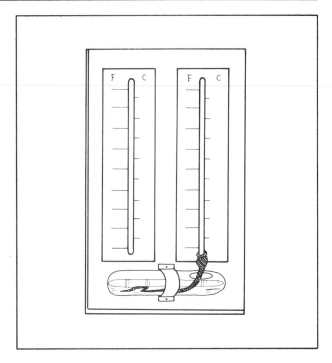

The drawing shows a very accurate hygrometer that measures relative humidity to within one percentage point.

 RULE OF THUMB: A vent fan offers the best value to control humidity in most gardens.

The HID lamp and ballast radiate dry heat, which lowers humidity. Dry heat from the HID system and a vent fan are usually all the humidity control necessary. Other dry heat sources, such as a heat vent from the furnace or wood stove, work well to lower humidity. If using forced air from a furnace to lower humidity, make sure warm, dry air does not blow directly on plants. This dry air will dehydrate plants rapidly.   One gardener sets out about 100 small silicon packets to absorb excess moisture in the small grow room.

Humidity is easily increased by misting the air with water or setting a bucket of water out to evaporate into the air. Draping a cheesecloth over the grill of a fan will buffer the breeze of a circulation fan over tender plants. This same principle can be used to make a simple but effective humidifier.   Simply   place a wick between the cheesecloth and a container of water. The cloth wick draws water up onto the cheesecloth. The fan will blow the moisture into the air. A humidifier are available retail for $100 to $150. The humidifier is essentially a fan over a bucket of water, controlled by a humidistat. The fan help evaporate water vapor into the air. A humidifier is usually not necessary unless there is an extreme problem with the room drying out. A dehumidifier removes moisture in a room. These units are a bit more complex, since the water must be condensed from the air. A dehumidifier can be used anytime to help guard against fungus. Just set the dial at the desired percent humidity and presto, perfect humidity. They cost from $150 to $200, but are worth the money to gardeners with extreme humidity problems. The best price on dehumidifiers has been found at discount retail stores. Dehumidifiers can also be rented if needed for only a month or two. Young seedlings and rooting cuttings grow better when the humidity is between 70 and 80 percent. Under arid conditions, the underdeveloped root system is not able to supply water fast enough. High humidity prevents dehydration.

Fan

Thermostat   Humidistat   Plug

The simple diagram above shows how to wire a vent fan to a thermostat and a humidistat. The fan will vent the room when either the humidistat or thermostat activate.

CO$_2$ Enrichment

Carbon dioxide (CO$_2$) is a colorless, odorless, non-flammable, non-toxic gas. The air we breathe contains .03 to .04 percent CO$_2$. Plants use all of the available CO$_2$ in an enclosed grow room rapidly. Photosynthesis and growth slow to a crawl when the CO$_2$ level falls below .02 percent.

CO$_2$ enrichment has been used in commercial greenhouses since the 1960's. It makes more CO$_2$ available to plants, stimulating growth. Indoor cultivation is similar greenhouse growing, and the same principles can be applied to the indoor garden. Plants are able to use more CO$_2$ than the .03 to .04 percent that naturally occurs in the air. By increasing the amount of CO$_2$ to .10 to .15 percent (1000 to 1500 parts per million (ppm)), plants may grow two to three times as fast, providing that light, water, and nutrients are not limiting. CO$_2$ enrichment has little or no effect on plants grown under fluorescent lights. The tubes do not supply enough light for the plant to process the extra available CO$_2$. On the other hand, HID lamps supply ample light to process the enriched CO$_2$ air. In a grow room using an HID light source, CO$_2$-enriched air, adequate water and nutrients, unbelievable results can be achieved. In fact, with this basic combination, plants grow much faster and more efficiently than outdoors under ideal conditions.

The demands of CO$_2$-enriched plants are much greater than normal, and plants require increased maintenance. They use nutrients, water and space about twice as fast as normal. A higher temperature range, from 75 to 85^0 F (24 to 30^0 C), will help stimulate more rapid chemical processes within the super plants. Properly maintained, they will grow so fast and take up so much space that flowering will have to be induced sooner than normal.

In fact, some people get frustrated using CO$_2$. It causes plants to grow so fast, that unsuspecting gardeners are unable to keep up with them. With CO$_2$-enriched air, plants that do not have the support of the other critical elements for life will not benefit from the CO$_2$. The plant can be limited by just one of the critical factors. For example, the plants use water and nutrients much faster. If these are not adequately supplied, plants will not grow faster. They may even be stunted if plants need a larger pot but are not transplanted get it soon enough, they will be runts.

 RULE OF THUMB: CO$_2$ enrichment requires more garden maintenance and moving up the garden calendar one to four weeks.

Increasing light intensity by adding another HID lamp helps speed growth, but might not be necessary. Check with the light meter to see if plants really need more light. The extra lamp could make the garden grow so fast that it is impossible to keep. More CO$_2$ does not require more hours of light per day. The photoperiod must remain the same as under normal conditions for healthy growth and flowering.

To be most effective, the CO_2 level must be kept near .10 to .15 percent everywhere in the room. To accomplish even distribution of CO_2, the grow room must be completely enclosed. Cracks in and around the walls over one-eighth-inch should be sealed off to prevent CO_2 from escaping. Enclosing the room makes it easier to control the CO_2 content of the air within. The room must also have a vent fan with flaps or a baffle. The vent fan will remove the stale air that will be replaced with CO_2-enriched air. The flaps or baffle will help contain the CO_2 in the enclosed grow room and prevent cool .backdrafts Venting requirements will change with each type of CO_2 enrichment system. Venting is discussed in detail in the "CO_2 Generator" and "Compressed CO_2 Gas" sections below.

Some of the problems associated with keeping the number of CO_2 constant in the air are the amount of plants in the room and the rate at which these plants are growing. If the plants are growing rapidly and are tightly packed into a leaky room, the CO_2 level will be difficult to maintain using the information provided by measuring the amount of CO_2 produced. If the temperature climbs to 80 or 90^0 F (27 to 32^0 C), the CO_2 is diluted in the air and it must be increased. A room that is not tightly sealed could use as much as 50 percent more CO_2.

Producing CO_2

There are many ways to increase the CO_2 content of an enclosed grow room. CO_2 is one of the by-products of combustion. Any hydrocarbon fuel can be burned to produce CO_2, except for those containing sulfur dioxide and ,ethylene which can be harmful to plants. See "CO_2 Generators" below. A by-product of fermentationand organic decomposition is CO_2 gas. The CO_2 level near the ground of a rain forest covered with decaying organic matter could be two to three times as high as normal. A by-product of decomposition is CO_2. But bringing a compostpile indoors to cook down is not practical.

Dry ice is made from frozen CO_2. The CO_2 is released when it comes in contact with the atmosphere. It can get expensive, and can be a lot of trouble keeping a large room replenished with

dry iceThere are lots of spin-offs to all of these principles and they all work in varying degrees. It is difficult to calculate how much CO_2 is released into the air by ,fermentation decomposition or dry ice without using very expensive equipment to measure it. Dry ice can get very expensive when used for a long time. Two pounds of wdry iceill raise the CO_2 level in 10-by-10-foot grow room to about 2000 ppm. for 24 hours. One chagrinned gardener remarked: "I can't believe that stuff melts so fast."

A decaying compostpile is out of the question indoors! Besides, a new compostpile would have to be moved twice a day to release enough CO_2.

Fermentationis an acceptable way to produce CO_2, but it is difficult to measure how much is produced. Here is a recipe for brewing CO_2. Use a one-gallon plastic milk jug or any gallon container to mix one cup of sugar and a packet of brewers yeast with about three quarts of warm water. The concoction smells horrid, but produces an initial burst of CO_2. Fermentationis one of the least expensive ways to produce CO_2, but it works best when used in a small growth chamber.

The CO_2 produced by fermentationis soon released in the enclosed chamber. The concoction is changed one to four times daily. Half of the solution is poured out, then 1 1/2 quarts of water and another cup of sugar are added. If the yeast does not continue to grow during the fermentationprocess, add another packet of yeast. The mix is similar to a sourdough starter mix. Try to keep it from dying. As long as the yeast continues to grow, the mix can be used indefinitely to generate CO_2. In fact, if a gardener were really into it, there could be several gallons and one would be changed every couple of hours. But smell would soon gag a maggot!

This CO_2 generator from Green Air Products will heat as well as produce carbon dioxide for the grow room.

CO$_2$ Generators

Commercial nurseries produce CO$_2$ with large generators. The generators produce CO$_2$ by using propane, butane or natural gas to burn oxygen out of the air in a chamber. The CO$_2$-rich air is then circulated among the plants. Heat, CO$_2$ and water vapor are by-products of combustion. Each pound of fuel burned equals three pounds of CO$_2$, 1 1/2 pounds of water and approximately 22,000 BTU's (British Thermal Units) of heat. Small, one lamp grow rooms can burn ethyl or methyl alcohol in a kerosine lamp. In a 10-by-10-foot grow room, three ounces of fuel will produce about 2000 ppm of CO$_2$ in 24 hours.

Heat buildup makes large CO$_2$ generators impossible to use in the heat of summer. The CO$_2$ generators used in greenhouses are too large to be practical for the average grow room. Several Northwest companies manufacture small-scale CO$_2$ generators that are similar to the large commercial units. The leading company in the field is Green Air Products. The smaller CO$_2$ generators were designed for grow rooms of 1500 to 4000 cubic feet.

These CO$_2$ generators work very well for larger or cool grow rooms. The generators can create quite a bit of heat. Remember, each pound of gas burned will create about 22,000 BTU's and 1 1/2 pounds of water vapor. In a small room, the heat and moisture produced could make it impractical to use.

The CO$_2$ generators are of two basic designs. The first, pictured on page 96, is normally hung from the ceiling. CO$_2$-rich air is produced and cascades over the plants. This model uses a pilot light with a flow meter and burner. The inside of the generator is similar to a gas stove burner with a pilot light enclosed, in a protective housing. For safety's sake, the generator *must have* a top covering the open flame at all times. The unit is equipped with a safety valve and a pilot light. It can be operated manually or placed on the same timer as the lamp to function automatically. An oscillating fan is placed near the floor to keep the CO$_2$-rich air stirred up. Models are available for rooms from 1,500 to over 4,000 cubic feet.

The second model is placed on the floor and has a fan on the side of the burner housing. The fan circulates the warm CO$_2$-rich air among the plants. The unit has an electronic pilot light with a safety timer that is electronically controlled to relight safely if the flame blows out for any reason.

LP gas (propane) is readily available at gas stations; the tanks are easy to move when full and very light when empty.

Propane is readily available. LP gas tanks are easy to acquire and painless to fill, unlike the heavy, awkward, compressed CO$_2$ tanks discussed below.

New propane tanks are normally filled with an inert gas to protect them from rust. Empty the inert gas out before filling a new tank for the first time. The inert gas does not mix well with propane, nor will it burn.

> **Note**: Never over-fill the propane tank! The gas expands and contracts with temperature change.

Many people prefer to manufacture their own CO$_2$ generator. To make a CO$_2$ generator, find a heater that burns clean and has a knob to control the exact flame produced. A blue flame is produced by propane or natural gas that is burning clean. A yellow flame has unburned gas (creating lethal carbon monoxide) and needs more oxygen to burn clean. Good examples of homemade CO$_2$ generators are propane heaters, stoves or lamps. In fact, even a Coleman lantern works quite well, but it must be started and stopped manually. One gardener uses unleaded (white) gas rather than expensive Coleman fuel.

> **Note**: CO$_2$ is used by humans at low levels. Levels above .4 percent (4000 ppm) could be hazardous if inhaled for long. The CO$_2$ level is easy to control with the proper metering system. Besides being hazardous to people at high concentrations. CO$_2$ can become toxic to plants at levels above .2 percent (2000 ppm).
> A relatively small flame will alter the CO$_2$ level in an enclosed grow room. With the help of a vent fan, there is little chance of any CO$_2$ gas buildup. Apply a solution of 50 percent water and 50 percent concentrated dish soap to all connections to check for leaks. When the bubbles appear, gas is escaping. Never use a leaky system!

Unless your grow room is huge, you do not need to allow for CO$_2$ to be present in the air. This excess CO$_2$ will be compensated for by the CO$_2$ that leaks out the cracks in the walls and through open doors. The examples show how to figure out how much CO$_2$ to generate in a room.

First, the *total volume* of the room is determined. Next the amount of fuel burned to produce the desired amount of CO_2 is calculated.

To find out how much CO_2 it will take to bring the grow room up to the optimum level, figure the total volume of the grow room, then divide by the optimum level of CO_2.

Example:

TOTAL VOLUME = L X W X H
TOTAL VOLUME = 10' X 8' X 10'
TOTAL VOLUME = 800 cubic feet

OPTIMUM LEVEL = .0015

.0015 X 800 cubic feet = 1.2 cubic feet

It will take 1.2 cubic feet of CO_2 to bring the 800 cubic foot grow room up to the optimum level of 1,500 ppm.

Each pound of fuel (kerosene, propane or natural gas) burned produces approximately three pounds of CO_2. One-third of a pound (5.3 ounces), produces about one pound of CO_2. At 68^0 (20^0 C), one pound of CO_2 displaces 8.7 cubic feet.

Total amount of CO_2 needed / 8.7 X .33 = pounds of fuel.
1.2 / 8.7 X .33 = .045 pounds of fuel needed
.045 X 16 = .72 ounce of fuel

To measure the amount of fuel used, weigh the tank before it is turned on, use it for an hour, then weigh it again. The difference in weight is the amount of gas or fuel used.

It is easier to measure the amount of CO_2 produced rather than measuring the amount of CO_2 in the atmosphere of the grow room. There are no inexpensive measuring kits on the market to measure the atmospheric content of CO_2. The least expensive kit costs about 250 and each test requires chemicals that are in a glass tube. Each measuring tube costs about $5. These kits may be purchased from many of the hydroponic stores that advertise in *Growing Edge Magazine*.

Exact venting requirements are difficult to determine when using CO_2 generators. Since it is difficult to measure the exact amount of CO_2 present in the room, it is difficult to detect exactly how much to vent. The best way to figure out how much to vent a grow room would be to measure the amount of CO_2 present in the air, then vent the room accordingly. However, this practice is too expensive for most people. To vent a room using a CO_2 generator, wire a vent fan in line to a humidistat and thermostat (page 96). Set the humidistat at 50 percent relative humidity and the thermostat at 80^0 F (27^0 C). This will maintain the CO_2 close to the perfect level. If the vent fan is on all the time, something must be wrong! The fan should not come on more than once an hour for the CO_2 level to remain near the perfect level.

Compressed CO_2 gas (see below) generally works best in grow rooms smaller than 200 to 300 square feet. The CO_2 is injected into the room from the tank. It creates no heat and a meter controls the exact amount of CO_2 desired. A room could be virtually any size and the exact amount of CO_2 could be injected. CO_2 tanks reach a point of diminishing returns. That is, rooms over 1500 cubic feet allow more room for the heat produced by the CO_2 generator to dissipate. The CO_2 generator is also more cost-effective for larger rooms than compressed CO_2. Some people do not want any kind of an unattended flame burning in their home. Use the CO_2 burner only if you feel comfortable with it.

The CO_2 emitter should disperse the CO_2 near the top of the room, so that the heavier-than-air CO_2 can cascade over the plants to be more useful.

When venting a CO_2-enriched room, use a fan placed near the ceiling as far away as possible from the CO_2 source in the room. CO_2 is heavier than air. This way, it will not escape when the room is vented.

Compressed CO_2

Compressed CO_2 gas is very safe, versatile and easy to control. Compressed CO_2 enrichment systems contain a combination regulator/flow meter, solenoid valve, short-range timer and tank of compressed CO_2 gas. There is a very good book on CO_2 systems, explaining in detail how each component of the system works. It is a *Manual on the Use of CO_2 With Metal Halide Grow-Lights* and is available through Van Patten Publishing $3.50 (see order blank in the back of this book). This book also gives step-by-step instructions on how to build and set up your own CO_2 enrichment system.

Compressed CO_2 is stored in metal cylinders or tanks under high pressure. Small cylinders contain 20 pounds and larger tanks contain 50 pounds. The gas is kept between 1,600 and 2,200 pounds of pressure per square inch (PSI). The CO_2 gas passes out of the tank into the flow meter/regulator where the pressure is reduced to 10 to 200 PSI. The solenoid valve opens and closes to let the CO_2 into the room. Most flow meter/regulators emit 10 to 50 cubic feet of CO_2 per hour. If the flow meter/regulator were set at 10 cubic feet per hour and left on for half an hour, five cubic feet of CO_2 would enter the room. The total amount of CO_2 needed to bring the level up to 1500 ppm for a 10-by-10-by-8-foot grow room is 1.2 cubic feet. See the example on page 99.

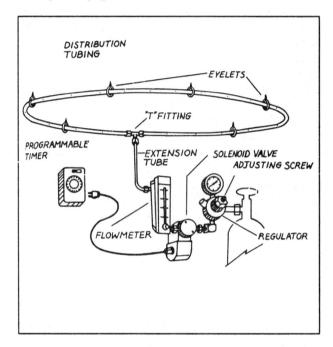

High tech CO_2 emitter developed by applied Hydroponics delivers a constant level of carbon dioxide to the grow room.

By altering the flow rate and time, the exact amount of CO_2 can be injected into the grow room.

For example:

Total amount of CO_2 needed / flow rate = time
1.2 / flow rate = time
1.2 / 10 = .12 hour
.12 hour X 60 minutes = 7.2 minutes

If the flow meter is set at 10 cubic feet per hour, the timer will need to be on 7.2 minutes to bring the CO_2 level up to the optimum 1500 ppm.

A short-range timer measures short periods of time accurately. Inexpensive 24-hour timers do not measure increments of time less than one hour accurately. If the short-range timer is set to be on for 7.2 minutes every few hours, the CO_2 level of the room will go up to the optimum level, then taper off until the next burst of CO_2 is injected. It is a good idea to split the 7.2 minutes down into smaller

increments so there is a regular supply of CO_2 in the room.

Vent the room using compressed CO_2 about 10 minutes before more CO_2 is injected into the room. Make sure the vent fan is not on while the CO_2 is being injected into the room, and for at least an hour afterward.

To vent the room with a ventilation fan, the CO_2-enriched room should have the vent high in the room. The vent provides fresh, cool air without removing the CO_2 that is heavier than air.

Negative Ions

A deionizer or negative ion generator makes negative ions, which purify the air and remove odors. They produce a negative electrical charge or negative ions. The negative ions pour out into the air. They seek out and attach themselves to positively charged particles (pollutants, fungus spores and odors) in the air. When a negative ion attaches to a positive ion, a neutral ion is created.

A negative ion generator will keep grow rooms smelling fresh.

Just after a rain storm, the air is packed with negative ions. The air feels still and smells fresh. Negative ion generators create this same atmosphere in your grow room. Plants grown in such an environment are generally very healthy. The generator uses very little electricity and plugs into a regular 110-volt electrical household outlet.

Visually check the filter every few days and make sure to keep it clean.

Exhaust fans are rated by the of cubic feet of air they can displace, or move, in a minute (CFM).

RULE OF THUMB: Use a vent fan that is able to replace all of the air in the grow room in five minutes or less.

Setting Up the Vent Fan

STEP ONE: Calculate the total volume of the grow room. Length X width X height = total volume. A grow room 10-by-10-by-8-feet has a total volume of 800 cubic feet (10' X 10' X 8' = 800 cubic feet)

STEP TWO: Find a vent fan that will remove the total volume of air from the room in five minutes or less. Buy a fan that can be mounted easily to the wall (8-inch fans are a favorite for larger rooms) or attached to the flexible 4-inch dryer hose. A high-speed squirrel-cage fan is necessary to maintain enough air flow through 4-inch flexible duct.

A wall fan built into an open window and a squirrel cage fan attached to a flexible four-inch plastic hose are two easy ways to vent the grow room.

STEP THREE: Place the fan high on a wall or near the ceiling of the grow room so that it vents off hot, humid air.

A vent fan is easily vented out the chimney of a basement using 8-inch stove pipe.

STEP FOUR: If possible, cut a hole in the wall and secure the fan in place over the hole. Do not worry about the hole, it can be patched, and the garden will breathe a breath of fresh air. However, most locations require special installation. See steps 5-9 below.

STEP FIVE: Placing a fan in a window helps prevent backdrafts. Cut a quarter-inch piece of plywood to fit the window sill. Cover the window with a light-proof black paint or similar covering. Mount the fan in the top of the plywood, to vent to the outside. Secure the plywood and fan in the window sill and open the window from the bottom.

STEP SIX: Another option that causes minimal backdraft is to use a 4-inch flexible clothes dryer hose. Vent the hose outdoors and attach a small squirrel-cage fan to the other end of the hose. Make sure there is a tight connection between the fan and the hose by using a large hose clamp. A dryer hose wall outlet with a flap will help decrease backdrafts.

STEP SEVEN: Another option is to vent the air up the chimney. If using the chimney for a vent flue, first clean the excess ash and creosote from the inside. Tie a chain to a rope. Lower the chain down the chimney, banging and knocking all debris inside to the bottom. There should be a door at the bottom of the chimney to remove the debris. This door can also be used as the vent hole.

STEP EIGHT: The fan can be attached to a thermostat and humidistat to vent hot, humid air outside when necessary. Instructions are available with the thermostats to wire it to the vent fan. The diagram on page 96 shows how to wire a thermostat and humidistat to the same fan.

STEP NINE: Attach the vent fan to a timer so that it runs for a specific length of time. This method is popular when used in conjunction with CO_2 enrichment. The fan is set to turn on and vent out used air just before new CO_2-rich air is injected.

Chapter Seven

Insects and Fungi

Insects will creep into your garden, eat, reproduce and be merry. Insects live everywhere outdoors. Indoors, insects will live just about anywhere that you (Mother Nature) let them. Fungus is present in the air at all times. It can be introduced by an infected plant or blow in with air containing fungus spores. Fungus will settle down and grow if climatic conditions are right. Both fungus and insects can be prevented, but once an infestation has started, severe methods of control may be necessary to eradicate them.

Insect Prevention

Cleanliness is the key to insect and fungus prevention. The grow room should be totally enclosed, so the environment can be easily controlled. Keep the floor clean. Keep all debris off soil surface. Do not use mulch. Bugs and fungus like nice hideaway places such as dirty corners, old damp leaves and mulch. You, the horticulturist, and your tools could be the transporters of many microscopic insects and fungi that may be fatal to the garden. Thoroughly wash and disinfect all new plants that will be moved into the grow room.

These plants are the potential carriers of devastating diseases. This does not mean you and your tools have to be hospital-clean every time you enter the grow room.

It does mean that normal and regular sanitary precautions do need to be taken. Wear clean clothes and use clean tools. Have a separate indoor set of tools to be used *only* in the grow room. Disinfect tools by dipping them in rubbing alcohol, or wash with soap and water after use a diseased plant. Bugs and fungus love to ride from plant to plant on dirty tools.

Personal cleanliness is very important for insect and fungus prevention. Wash your hands before handling plants and after handling diseased plants. Do not walk around your buggy outdoor garden, then visit your indoor garden; do it vice versa. Think before entering the indoor garden and possibly contaminating it. Did you walk across a lawn covered with rust (rust is a rust-colored fungus) or pet the dog that just came in from the garden outside? Did you just fondle your spider-mite-infested split-leaf philodendron in the living room?

Once you have grown an annual crop in a potting soil or soilless mix, throw it out. Some gardeners have used the same old potting soil over and over with acceptable results. They place charcoal in the bottom of containers to absorb excess salts and maintain sweet soil. Used soil makes excellent outdoor garden soil. Used soil may harbor harmful insects and fungi that have developed an immunity to sprays. Starting a new crop in new potting soil will cost more initially, but will eliminate many potential problems.

Once potting soil is used it compacts easily and the texture is poor. Roots have trouble penetrating compacted soil, and there is little room for oxygen, which restricts root respiration. Used potting soil is depleted of valuable N-P-K nutrients as well as secondary and trace elements. A plant with a slow start in poor soil is a perfect target for disease.

Companion planting works to discourage insects. Bugs, except for thrips, hate garlic. Garlic is readily available, take up little room, transplant well and discourage insects. Garlic is the best companion plant for indoor vegetables or flowers. When sowing seeds or transplanting, just plant a few cloves of garlic about a half-inch deep alongside. They sprout and grow in a week or two, driving insects away. Garlic will grow straight up, creating very little shade, and has a compact root system attached to the bulb below the soil. When transplanting, just move garlic along with the vegetable or flower. Garlic is very resilient, withstanding more shock during transplanting than most vegetables or flowers. Vegetables are usually harvested before the garlic matures. These garlic plants may be transplanted to companion other young plants through life. It is a good idea to dip the garlic transplant into an insecticide/fungicide solution to prevent transferal of disease.

Marigolds also discourage insects, but not as well as garlic. Marigolds are much prettier than garlic, but they must be blooming to effectively discourage insects above the soil.

Plant insect- and fungus-resistant strains of flowers and vegetables. Most seed houses supply seed that is resistant to insect and fungus attacks. When choosing your parent plants for vegetative propagation, inspect them regularly and compare them to one another for insect and fungus resistance. Some plants of the same variety attract insects and disease and may be infested, while others growing nearby have little or no problem at all.

Keep plants healthy and growing fast at all times. Disease attacks sickly plants first. Strong plants tend to grow faster than insects can eat or fungus can spread. With strong, healthy, fast-growing plants, a few insects or a little fungus does very little damage.

Forced-air circulation makes life miserable for insects and fungus. Bugs hate wind; they cannot hold on to the plants or fly very well in a windy environment. Fungus has little time to settle in a breezy room. Nor does fungus grow well on wind-dried soil, stems and leaves.

Ventilation will change the humidity of a room quickly. In fact, a vent fan attached to a humidistat is the most foolproof form of humidity control. One gardener was having a big problem with mold in a grow room that did not have a vent fan. It was terrible! Upon entering the enclosed grow room, with the humidity near 100 percent, eyeglasses would steam up immediately. The room was so humid that roots were growing from the stems of plants. The gardener installed a vent fan, which drew the moist, stale air from the grow room, venting it outdoors. The mold problem disappeared.

Every indoor gardener should practice all of the preventative measures. It is much easier to prevent a disease from getting started than it is to wipe out an infestation. If insects or fungus multiply and are left unchecked, the entire garden could be devastated in a few weeks.

Insect Control

Sometimes, even with all preventive measures taken, insects and fungus still sneak in and set up housekeeping. First they will establish themselves on a weak, susceptible plant, then launch an all-out assault on the rest of the garden. They will move out in all directions from the infested base, taking over more and more space, until they have conquered the entire garden. This can happen in a matter of days. Bugs can lay thousands of eggs that grow into mature adults within a few weeks. For example, say you failed to take preventive measures or closely examine plants for disease, and 100 microscopic munchers each laid 1000 eggs, which grew into adults two weeks later. By the end of the month, there would be millions of insects attacking the infested garden.

Sprays essentially kill adults and, all too often, only some of them. Sprays should be applied soon after eggs hatch, so young adult insects are caught in their weakest stage of life. Horticultural oil and insecticidal soap spray works well alone or as an additive to help kill larvae.

The availability of sprays can be seasonal. Garden sections of stores change to sell other merchandise for the winter. The garden stock is sometimes kept in the storage room, but much of it is sold in a season-end sale. Excellent bargains on sprays and other garden items are available for the winter growing season at these season-end sales.

The products recommended in this book work and are readily available. This does not mean they are the best or the only products to use. There are many local products that are just as good as national or Northwest brands.

Insects

The indoor gardener has many options to control insects and fungi. Prevention is at the top of the list. There is a logical progression to insect and fungus control that is outlined in the chart below. Notice that it starts with cleanliness and progresses through the most basic elements.

RULE OF THUMB: Follow the logical progression for insect and fungi control.

Manual removal is just what the name implies: smashing all insects in sight between the thumb and forefinger, or between two sponges. Make sure not to infect other plants with filthy hands or sponges.

Logical Progression of Insect Control

1. Prevention
   cleanliness
   use new soil
   indoor set of tools
   disease resistant plants
   healthy plants
   climate control
   no animals
2. Manual removal
   fingers
   sponges
3. Organic sprays
4. Natural preditors

If you must use a spray, always use a natural one. Harsh chemicals are only a last resort. With the development of an environmental consciousness and technology, several new natural-based sprays have been developed. They offer unique qualities unknown to harsh chemical sprays. As with any spray, always seems to slow plants down a little, even if it is natural. The plant is covered with the filmy residue of the spray. The stomata are clogged until the spray wears off or is washed off. Try to spray the plants only when necessary. Please read "About Spraying" (pages 116-118) at the end of this chapter. Read *all* the labels of all sprays thoroughly before you use them. Use only contact sprays for

edible plants. Systemic sprays can be used for ornamental plants. Do not use any sprays at all on young seedlings or tender cuttings. The spray could burn or kill the tender little plant.

Organic Pesticides

Botanical sprays are made from plants and naturally occurring substances. Some botanicals are toxic to insects and others are just offensive, discouraging their presence.

Bacillus thuringiensis or *Bt*

Bacillus thuringiensis commonly referred to as *Bt* is a disease-causing bacteria. The caterpillar or worm first eats the *Bt* and within a short time the digestive system becomes paralyzed. Many pests are affected including cabbage loopers, cabbage worms, corn earworms, cutworms, Gypsy moth larvae, hornworms, some nematodes and tent caterpillars. *Bt* is sold as a dormant spore dust or a liquid under the names of Dipel, Biotrol, or Thuricide.

Bt/H-14 sold under the trade names Vectobac and Gnatrol controls destructive soil nematodes. Destructive nematodes are difficult to see. They cause slow growth and slowly rotting roots.

All of the strains of *bacillus thuringiensis* are nontoxic to humans, animals and plants.

Diatomaceous Earth

Diatomaceous (DE) earth is formed by the lacy shells of trillions of minute one celled silicate algae (diatoms) that have died and settled to the bottom of oceans or lake beds. These prehistoric lightweight snowflake-like skeletons have been fossilized. They form deposits hundreds of feet thick that are mined, pulverized and sold as a non-toxic wettable powder that is fatal to most soft bodied insects including aphids, slugs and spider mites. Some beneficial insects are also subject to the piercing DE. The diotomaceous earth (DE) works by puncturing or slicing the pest's body, causing dehydration. If the pest ingests the razor-sharp diatomaceous earth, it disrupts vital body functions. Earthworms, animals, humans and birds however, can digest diatomaceous earth and are not effected by it. DE also contains 14 trace minerals in a chelated (available) form.

> Use a protective mask when openly handling this fine powder to guard against irritations.

Spread DE in a quarter-inch deep, two-inch wide border to prevent slugs and snails from crossing over to eat plants. Mix 1 part DE with 3 to 5 parts water and a few drops of biodegradable dish soap to use as a spray. Apply this spray to infestations of pest insects. A dusting of DE is most effective. Use a ketchup bottle or commercial duster to apply DE dust to the undersides of moist foliage. The dust sticks to the moist leaves where it stays until washed off by rain or irrigation. For best results, do not water for 48 hours after application.

Caution! Do not use swimming pool diotomaceous earth. It is chemically treated and heated, This product contains crystalline silica that is hazardous if inhaled. The body is unable to dissolve the crystalline form of silica which causes chronic irritation.

Homemade Sprays

Many homemade spray preparations are outstanding insecticides. A hot taste or smelly odor are the main principles behind most home-brewed potions. The sprays are normally made by mixing repellent plants with a little water in a blender. The resulting slurry concentrate is strained through a nylon stocking or fine cloth before being diluted with water for application.

Cooking or heating preparations generally destroys active ingredients. To draw out ingredients, mince plant and soak in a mineral oil for a couple of days. Add this oil to the water including a little soap to emulsify the oil.

Any nondetergent, biodegradable soap will work as a wetting and sticking agent in these preparations. The soap dissolves best if a teaspoon of alcohol is added to each quart of water.

Camomile sprays are used to prevent dampening-off and mildew.

Chrysanthemum, marigold and nasturtium blossoms, garlic, chive, onion, hot pepper, bug juice, horseradish, mints, oregano, tomato and tobacco residues repel or kill many insects including aphids, caterpillars, mites and whiteflies. Be very careful with tobacco sprays. (See "Nicotine & Tobacco Sprays" page 106). These mixes can vary in proportions, but the blended remaining slurry is always filtered before adding with water for the final spray.

One homemade organic spray is made by blending 1 teaspoon of hot pepper or Tabasco sauce, 4 cloves of garlic with a quart of water. Grind this mix up in the blender and strain through a nylon stocking or cheese cloth before using in the sprayer.

A mix of one eighth to one quarter cup of hydrated lime mixed with a quart of water makes an effective insect spray and is especially effective on tiny insects such as spider mites. Mix a nondetergent soap with the lime; the soap acts as both a sticking agent and insecticide. Lime can be caustic in large doses. Always try the spray on a test plant and wait a few days to check for adverse effects before applying to other plants.

Another natural spray is made from chopped tomato leaves soaked in water. The water is used as a spray against white cabbage butterflies.

Spray made out of bug guts ground up in a blender, emulsified in water.

Hot Pepper Wax

Hot pepper wax is ont of the newest insecticides on the market. It has been very effective against aphids and spider mites. The substance is nontoxic to plants and people. Hot pepper wax is available at some of the hydroponic stores that advertise in *Growing Edge Magazine.*

Insecticidal Soaps

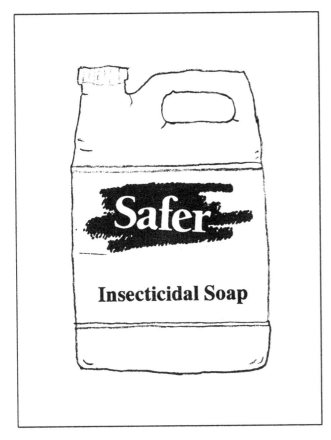

Insecticidal soaps are mild contact insecticides made from fatty acids of animals and plants. These soaps are safe for bees, honeybees, animals and humans. The soap controls soft-bodied insects such as aphids, mealybugs, spider mites, thrips and whiteflies by penetrating and destroying body membranes.

Safer's Insecticidal Soap is the first and best known soap. It is a potassium-salt based liquid concentrate that is toxic to insects but not to animals or humans.

Soft soaps such as Ivory liquid dish soap or Castille's soap are biodegradable and kill insects in the same manor as Safer's, but they are not as potent. Do not use detergent soaps, they may be caustic. Add a few cap-fulls of Ivory or Castille's to a quart of water and spray. These soaps can also be used as a wetting agent when watering down peat moss, dry potting soil or seedlings. The soap reduces the surface tension of the water to give it better penetration. Ivory or Castille's can also be used as a spreader-sticker to mix with sprays. The soaps help the spray stick to the foliage better, which is important when using contact sprays. The soft soaps will only last for about one day before dissipating.

Nicotine (sulfate) and Tobacco Sprays

Nicotine is a non-persistent pesticide derived from tobacco. It is toxic to most all insects and humans if a concentrate is swallowed. Many times nicotine is mixed with sulfur. One well known brand on the market is Black Flag's Nicotine Sulfate.

Nicotine sulfate (tobacco juice mixed with sulfur) is an excellent insecticide on all plants except members of the nightshade family (eggplant, tomatoes, peppers and potatoes). You can purchase bottled nicotine sulfate or simply use tobacco diluted in water. Apply the nicotine as a spray to kill aphids and whiteflies.

In small concentrations, nicotine sulfate is not toxic to humans.

Horticultural Oil

Oil spray is a safe, non-poisonous and non-polluting insecticide. Similar to medicinal mineral oil, it kills slow moving and immobile sucking insects by smothering and suffocating them while the thin oily film remains invisible to humans. Oil spray control for aphids, scale, spider mites and thrips.

Pyrethrum

This extremely powerful insecticide is extracted from the flowers of the pyrethrum chrysanthemum (*Chrysanthemum coccineum* and *C. cinergrii folium*), grown commercially in the tropical mountains of Ecuador and Kenya. A broad-spectrum pesticide pyrethrum is very toxic to most insects, including beneficials and cockroaches. If applied as a spray, pyrethrum is very effective to control flying insects. But if the insect does not receive a killing dose, they may revive. For this reason, pyrethrum is often combined with rotenone or ryana to ensure pest death. Use this non-selective insecticide to spot spray only heavily infested plants.

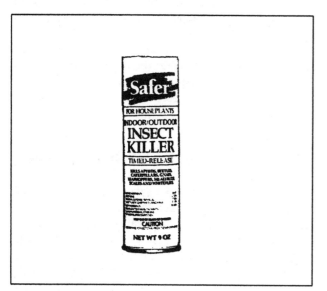

Pyrethrum

Pyrethrum is not toxic to animals or humans. Purchase in aerosol, dust or liquid. Aerosol spray is very convenient, but can burn foliage if applied closer than one foot. Aerosols also contain piperonyl butoxide which is toxic to people. All forms of pyrethrum dissipates within a few hours in the presence of air and HID light. At least one manufacturer offers an encapsulated pyrethrum in aerosol form. As the spray fogs out of the nozzle, a bubble forms around each droplet of mist. The outside coating keeps the pyrethrum intact for several days. If an insect should encounter the bubble, pop! The pyrethrum is released.

Sulfur

Sulfur is a common fungicide that has been used for centuries. If you should need to use this strong fungicide, apply it in *very* light concentrations. Sulfur easliy burns foliage. Be careful.

Traps

Black lights can be used to catch egg-laying moths. Light and fan traps attract many insects including beneficials and their use may do more harm than good.

When using sex lure traps, place them away from sensitive plants so insects will be lured away from them.

Safer's Housefly Trap   Sticky traps

Sticky "tanglefoot" resins can be smeared on attractive yellow or red cards to simulate ripe fruit. When the pests land on the "fruit" they are stuck forever!

A simple screen placed over a bucket or jar of sweetened water makes an excellent insect trap. Pour some water into a bucket and sweeten it with molasses or sugar and include some protein like powdered egg or yeast. Pests such as corn borers, cucumber beetles, cutworms, tomato horn worms, cucumber beetles and more are attracted to this sweet trap.

Handpick: Drop pest insects in a jar of paint thinner, kerosine topped water or salt water.

Predators

A predator may be a small parasite that enters the host's body, to eat it from the inside out. Or it can be a huge insect that devours many victims daily. The rate at which the predators keep the infestation in check is directly proportionate to the amount of predators. The more predators, the sooner they will take care of any infestations. Predators breed faster than their victim. The predators are the crusading warriors in the never-ending battle of pest-free horticulture.

One of the best outlets in the country to buy predatory insects is from Natures Control, Medford, Oregon. This supplier (Don Jackson) gives good advice and sends along specific instructions as well as a brochure about all the predators he offers. Another excellent supplier, AGS, 297 N. Barrington Road, Streamwood, IL

60107. Predators are shipped special delivery and may arrive after the daily mail delivery. The inside of a mailbox in the hot sun easily reaches 120^0 F (49^0 C) can be below freezing in winter. Check the mailbox regularly if ordering predators.

When any predator is introduced into the garden, there must be special precautions taken to ensure their well-being. Stop spraying all toxic chemicals and organic sprays at least two weeks before introducing the predators. Pyrethrum and Safer's Insecticidal Soap can be applied up to a few days before, providing any residue is washed off with water. Do not spray at all for 30 days after releasing predators.

Most of the predators that do well in the HID garden cannot fly. Bugs that can fly usually go straight for the lamp. The ladybug is a good example. If 500 ladybugs are released on Monday, by Friday, only a few die-hards will be left; the rest will have flown into the hot lamp and died. If using flying predators, release them when it is dark. They will last longer.

Predators are usually very small and must be introduced to each plant separately. This could take a little time and patience, so budget enough time. Predators also have specific climatic requirements. For best results, pay close attention; note the predator's needs and maintain them.

Oil sprays are widely used in greenhouses. They are not the same kinds of oils used in the car or sold at the hardware store. Do not use 3-in-1 oil or anything similar in place of horticultural petroleum oil. Horticultural oil is refined by removing most of the portion that is toxic to plants. Make sure it is a lightweight horticultural oil with a viscosity of 60 to 70. The lighter the oil, the less toxic it is to plants. Use oil sprays only during vegetative growth. This way, the residue has ample time to dissipate before harvest.

Mix two drops of oil spray (no more than a one-percent solution) per quart of water. More than a few drops could burn tender growing shoots and clog stomata. Repeat applications as needed, usually three applications, one every five to 10 days will do it. The first application will kill most of the adults and many eggs. Eggs hatch in about 10 days. The second spraying will kill the newly hatched eggs and the remaining adults. The third application will finish off any survivors.

Bug bombs are very strong insecticides that essentially exterminate everything living in the room They were developed to kill fleas and roaches. Bug bombs are used between crops to rid the grow room of all insects before introducing the next crop. Many manufacturers produce bug bombs under various brand names containing a wide variety of toxic chemicals.

Place the bug bomb in the empty room. Turn it on. Then leave the room. The chemicals are very toxic! Follow directions to the letter!

Spider Mites

The spider mite is the most common insect found on flowers and vegetables indoors. (Actually, it is not really an insect, it is a spider. Insects have six legs and spiders have eight.) These microscopic mites are found on the leaf's undersides, sucking away the plant's life-giving fluids. To the untrained eye, they are very difficult to spot. Most people notice the tell-tale yellowish-white spots (stippling) on the tops of the leaves first. More careful inspection will reveal tiny spider webs on the stems and under leaves. Webs may easily be seen when leaves are misted with water. The spider mites appear as tiny specks on leaf undersides. The naked eye has a hard time distinguishing the pests; nonetheless, they can be seen. A magnifying glass or low power microscope helps to identify the yellow, white, two-spotted, brown or red mites and their light-colored eggs.

Control: has a logical progression. First make sure all preventative measures have been taken.

Note: The spider mite thrives in a dry - 70 to 80^0 F (21 to 27^0 C). It can reproduce in five days if the temperature is above 80^0 F (27^0 C).

In order to create a hostile environment for mites, lower the temperature to 60^0 (15^0 C) and spray the plants with a jet of water, making sure to spray under leaves. This will blast them off the leaves as well as increase humidity. Their reproductive cycle will be slowed and you will have a chance to kill them before they do much damage. If the leaves have been over 50 percent damaged, remove and throw away, making sure insects and eggs do not re-enter the garden. If mites have attacked only one or two plants, isolate the infected plants and treat them separately. Once a hostile environment and leaves over 50 percent infected have been removed, the horticulturist may select one or more of the following control methods:

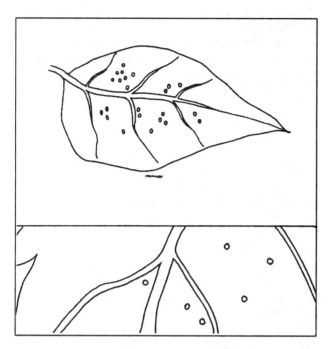

Mite eggs above look like translucent dots on the leaf underside. The bottom photo shows a close up of stripping caused by spider mites.

Manual removal: Smash all mites in sight between your thumb and index finger or wash leaves individually with two sponges.

Homemade sprays work very well when there is not yet an infestation of mites. If these sprays have not eradicated the mites after four or five applications, switch to another, stronger spray.

Insecticidal soaps are wonderful products that control mites fairly well. Usually two or three heavy applications at intervals of five to 10 days will do the trick.

Pyrethrum (aerosol) is the best natural a miticide. Two or three applications at intervals of five to 10 days usually stops mites dead.

Predatory spider mites work very well. There are many things to consider when using the predators. First and foremost, predators only can eat about 20 eggs or five adults daily. This gives you an idea of how fast they can really control the spider mites, which are their only source of food. As soon as the predators' source of food is gone, they cannibalize one another or die of starvation. A general dosage of 20 predators per plant is a good place to start. You might even want to throw in a few more for good measure. Spider mites have a difficult time traveling from plant to plant, so setting them out on each plant is necessary. Temperature and humidity are the most important factors to maintain. Both must be at the proper level to give the predators the best possible chance of survival. There are two kinds of predators commonly used indoors: *amblyseius californicus* and *phytoseiulus longipes*.

When spider mites have infested a garden, predatory mites can not eat them fast enough to solve the problem quickly. Predatory mites work best when there are only a few spider mites. The predators are introduced as soon as spider mites are seen, and released every month thereafter. This gives predators a chance to keep up with mites. Getting started with predatory mites will cost about $30. Before releasing predators, rinse all plants thoroughly to ensure that all toxic spray residues from insecticides and fungicides are gone.

Whiteflies

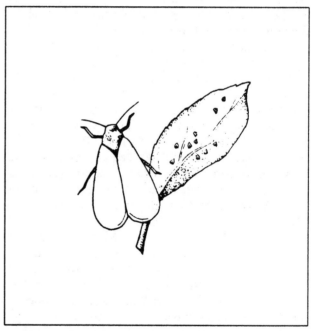

Whitefly

Whiteflies, also called leafhoppers, may cause white speckles (stipples) on the tops of leaves and hide underneath. The stipples are very similar to those made by spider mites. The easiest way to check for the little pests is to grab a limb and shake it. If there are any whiteflies, they will flutter from under leaves. An adult whitefly looks like a white moth about one millimeter long. They usually appear near the top of the weakest plant first. They will move downward on the plant or fly off to infest another plant.

Control: Take all preventive measures. Whiteflies are very difficult to remove manually;

they fly faster than the hand is able to squish them. Adults are attracted to the color yellow. To build a whitefly trap similar to flypaper, cover a bright yellow object with a sticky substance. Place the traps on the tops of the pots. The traps work very well, but are a mess to clean.

Whiteflies are easily eradicated with natural sprays. Before spraying, remove any leaves that have been over 50 percent damaged and cure with heat or burn.

Homemade sprays applied at intervals of two to 10 days work well.

Insecticidal soaps applied at intervals of five to 10 days.

Pyrethrum (aerosol) applied at intervals of two to 10 days does it.

The parasitic wasp, *encarsia formosa*, it the most effective whitefly predator. The small wasps attack only whiteflies. They do not sting people. As with all predators, all toxic sprays must be washed completely off before their introduction.

The *encarsia formosa* is a parasite, about an eighth-inch long and much smaller than the whitefly. This small predator takes several weeks longer to eliminate and control the whitefly population. Once the parasite penetrates the whitefly, death is slow. The parasite feeds for some time on the host insect, then its eggs hatch inside the victim's body cavity. If you use them, set them out at the rate of two or more parasites per plant as soon as the first whitefly is detected. Repeat every two to four weeks until thrips are controlled.

Aphids

Aphids are most common indoors when they are plentiful outdoors. About the size of a pinhead, aphids are easily spotted with the naked eye. This insect may be green, yellow, black or pink, and with or without wings. Aphids excrete a sticky honeydew and prefer to attack weak plants. They attack growing tips or buds first, sucking out fluids. Aphids love to hide on the leaves' undersides. An infestation of aphids can devastate a garden in a matter of days.

Control: Even though aphids may have wings, manual removal is easy and works well to kill them. They do not fly as well as whiteflies. Aphids bite into the plant, sucking out life-giving juices. When affixed to foliage, aphids are unable to move and easy to squish.

Homemade and Safer's sprays are very effective. Apply two or three times at intervals of

five to 10 days, after manually removing as many aphids as possible.

Pyrethrum (aerosol) applied two to three times at intervals of two to 10 days eradicates them.

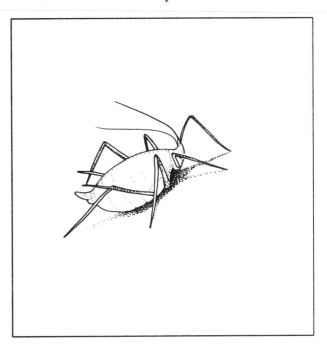

Aphid

Lacewing are the most effective available predators for aphids. Release one to 20 lacewing per plant, depending on infestation level, as soon as aphids appear. Repeat every month. If possible, buy adult lacewing rather than larvae, which take several weeks to hatch and mature into adult aphid exterminators.

Ladybugs (ladybird beetles) also work very well to exterminate aphids. Adults are easily obtained at many retail nurseries during the summer months and mail order the rest of the year. The only drawback to ladybugs is their attraction to the HID lamp. Release about 20 lady bugs per plant. About half of them will go directly for the HID, hit the hot bulb and buzzzz . . . Within a few weeks, all the ladybugs will fall victim to the lamp, requiring frequent replenishment.

Thrips

Thrips are not very common indoors. These tiny, winged, fast-moving creatures rasp on the leaves and buds, then suck out the juices for food. They tend to feed inside flower buds or wrap up and distort leaves. Thrips are not hard to spot.

Upon careful inspection, thrips appear as a herd of specks thundering across foliage.

Control: Preventive maintenance. Manual removal works if only a few thrips are present, but they are hard to catch.

Homemade sprays are very effective. Apply two to four times at intervals of five to 10 days.

Insecticidal soaps are very effective. Apply at intervals of two to 10 days.

Pyrethrum (aerosol) applied at intervals of two to 10 days does it.

Thrips have no readily available natural predators.

Thrip

Mealy Bugs

Mealy bugs are somewhat common. These oblong, waxy white insects, 2 to 7 millimeters long, move very little, mature slowly and live in colonies that are usually located at stem joints. Like aphids, mealy bugs excrete a sticky honeydew. Mealy bugs are easy to control, since they reproduce and move slowly.

Control: Preventive maintenance. Manual removal works very well for small populations. Pry them off by getting a fingernail underneath. Wet a Q-Tip with rubbing alcohol and touch them with it. The alcohol kills the mealy bugs quickly.

Homemade sprays work well, especially if they contain rubbing alcohol. Apply two or three times at intervals of five or 10 days.

Insecticidal soap applied at 5-10 day intervals kills mealy bugs in a day or two.

Mealy Bug

The ladybug (ladybird beetle) and the green lacewing are effective natural predators. Both work very efficiently and have no trouble eating mealy bugs faster than they can reproduce. If using these predators, manually remove all visible mealy bugs; release five to 10 predators per plant, depending on need, as soon as the mealy bugs are noticed. Repeat releases at two week intervals. Within a month, there should be a noticeable reduction in mealy bug population.

Many professionals prefer nicotine sulfate to control mealy bugs. Apply at intervals of five to 10 days. Do not use nicotine sulfite on tomatoes, peppers or eggplants. It will give them the fatal tobacco mosaic virus.

Scale

Scale is uncommon on many plants indoors. Scale looks and acts similar to mealy bugs, but is usually more round than oblong. Scale may be white, yellow, brown, gray or black. Their hard protective shell is 2 to 4 millimeters across and they rarely move. Check for mealy bugs around stem joints, where they live in colonies. Scale sometimes excretes a sticky honeydew.

Control: Preventive maintenance. Manual removal may be tedious, but is very effective. Wet a Q-Tip in rubbing alcohol and wash scale away. A small knife, fingernails or tweezers may also be necessary to scrape and pluck the tightly affixed scale from the plants.

Homemade sprays work well if they contain rubbing alcohol.

Insecticidal soaps work well to control scale. Apply at 10-day intervals.

Pyrethrum (aerosol) applied two or three times at intervals of 2 to 10 days does it.

Scale

Nature holds many natural scale predators, but to date there are no readily available commercial predators.

Bees, Flies etc.

Bees and wasps may become a nuisance. They are not harmful to plants but hurt when they sting you. They sneak into the grow room through vents or cracks, in search of flowering plants, a valuable commodity to bees and wasps in midwinter. Manual removal is out of the question! A circulation fan in the room is the best form of preventive maintenance. The artificial wind will impair their flight, causing them to seek a more hospitable garden. There are many aerosol sprays that kill bees and wasps. Wasp traps are also available. Sweet flypaper is also a good alternative. Bees and wasps are attracted to the HID lamp. Many will fall victim to its outer envelope....BUZZ...POP!

Fruit flies and gnats can become a problem. They do no harm to the indoor garden, but are a nuisance to be around. If you are impatient and the chore of cleaning up insect bodies is not appealing, just about any indoor insect spray in the aerosol form will get rid of them. One friend used one cup of Wisk per gallon of water to kill all the larvae in the soil.

Diseases, Fungi and Mold

Plant diseases are caused by bacteria, fungus, virus, other parasites or growth inhibiting environmental conditions.

Fungus is a very primitive plant. It is so primitive that it does not produce chlorophyll, the substance giving higher plants their green color. Fungi reproduce by spreading tiny microscopic spores rather than seeds. Many fungus spores are present in the air at all times. With proper conditions, spores will settle, take hold and start growing. Entire gardens have been wiped out in a matter of days by an uncontrolled outbreak of fungus. One grow room was close to a swamp filled with fungus spores. Unsterilized, soggy soil and humid, stagnant air provide the environment most fungi need to thrive. Although there are many different types of fungi, they are usually treated by the same methods.

Prevent diseases by avoiding conditions that cause them. Many plant diseases are caused by poor drainage, imbalanced soil fertility, inadequate air circulation, insect damage and unsanitary conditions. For example, aphids that pierce and suck plant juices, transmit viruses when they move from one plant to the next. The wounds aphids make begin to decay and become infected with airborne diseases.

Soil infertility and poor drainage are normally indicated by sickly plants that are prone to disease and insect attack. Throwing more fertilizers at the soil and trying to control pests on sickly plants may be more trouble than it is worth. In the case of poor soil, it is generally better to remove the sickly plants, replace the soil and start over with new, healthy plants.

You, the gardener, may be responsible for spreading diseases by handling wet diseased plants and touching uninfected plants. Whenever possible, work in the garden when foliage is dry; most bacteria and fungi need moisture to travel from one plant to another. Removing and destroying any diseased foliage and washing your hands afterward will go a long way to retain overall garden health.

Plant disease resistant varieties. New varieties that not only grow better in your climate but are much more resistant to disease. Years of careful breeding have given us all kinds of surprising plants.

Allow enough space between plants for air to circulate freely. Good air circulation prevents ever-present air-borne fungal spores from settling on foliage.

Plant diseases are more difficult to identify than insect attacks. They may start inside the plant or attack the roots and give little or no notice before killing plants. Many times by the time you notice a disease, it is too late to do anything about it. Other diseases such as gray mold or rust do show externally of foliage. They are much easier to identify and control.

Fungus Prevention

Prevention is the first step and the true key to fungus control. In "Setting Up the Grow Room," I recommended you remove anything that might attract fungus or harbor mold, such as cloth curtains or clothes. Make sure the advice is followed as part of a preventive program. If the room is carpeted, make sure to cover it with white plastic visqueen. If mold should surface on the walls, spray it heavily with the fungicide used in the garden, wash down the wall with Pinesol (made from natural pine oil) or paint damp, fungus covered walls with whitewash (page 52). Get all of the mold off when it is washed down. Repeat applications if the mold persists. The basic ingredients of mold and fungi control are cleanliness and climate control. Clean, well-ventilated grow rooms have little or no problem with fungi. Dingy, ill-kept gardens have fungus problems and yield sickly flowers and vegetables. If the garden is in a basement, the use of a flat white paint with a fungus-inhibiting agent is essential. One garden basement was carpeted with fungi. To combat fungus, the walls were whitewashed and lime was spread on the earth floor. The vent fan was turned

on 24 hours a day and the room kept clean. There has been no trouble with mold in the room in over a year.

There are many ways to lower humidity. Ventilation is the least expensive, easy and most often used. Remember, one of the by-products of burning a fossil fuel in CO_2 generators is water vapor. Dehumidifiers work exceptionally well, offering exact humidity control. They can be purchased or rented. Wood, coal, gas and electric heat all dehumidify the air. Many grow rooms have a central heating vent. This vent may be opened to provide additional heat and lower humidity.

Fungus Control

Fungus is prevented by controlling all the factors contributing to its growth. If prevention fails and fungus appears, the horticulturist should take control measures. Remove dead leaves and alter soil, moisture and air conditions to prevent fungus from spreading. These methods work well in gardens that have only a few signs of fungus. Another method of treating fungus is to isolate the infected plant and treat it separately. Fungus can spread like wildfire. If it gets a good start, take all preventive measures, as well as spraying the entire garden with a fungicide. Spraying will be necessary if the fungus gets a good start and appears to be spreading, even though preventive measures have been taken.

A natural fungicide.

Fungicides come in two basic categories: narrow-spectrum, specific against a few organisms, and broad spectrum, effective against numerous fungi.

Fungistats inhibit, but do not destroy fungi. These chemicals are used by busy growers to keep fungi in check.

Growers must alternate broad- and narrow-spectrum fungicides to effectively fight gray mold (*botrytis*), alternating or mixing combats resistance to the fungicide.

Copper and sulfur sprays, can be used safely in light mixtures. Be careful when using these fungicides, they can severely damage young tender growth.

When using a fungicide, spray the garden or plant at least twice, 5 to 10 days apart, even if you cannot see the fungus during the second or third spraying. The fungus spores can be present on the recently infected foliage, but not visible.

LOGICAL PROGRESSION OF FUNGUS CONTROL
1. Prevention 　　a. cleanliness 　　b. low humidity 　　c. ventilation 2. Remove infected foliage and plants 3. Copper, lime, sulfur or potassium based sprays

Damping-off

Damping-off is a soil-borne fungus that rots newly sprouted seedlings and occasionally attacks rooting cuttings at the soil line. The stem weakens, then grows dark at the soil line. Finally fluid circulation is cut, killing the seedling or cutting. Damping-off is normally caused by fungus already present in an unsterile rooting medium, over-watering, maintaining soggy soil, or excessive humidity.

To prevent all three conditions, use fresh, sterile soil or soilless mix and clean pots. This will guard against harmful fungus in the soil. Careful daily scrutiny of soil will ensure that the proper amount of moisture is available to seeds or cuttings. Many gardeners prefer to start seeds and root cuttings in fast-draining, sterile, coarse sand, fine vermiculite or rockwool cubes. Using these mediums makes it almost impossible to over-water. Do not place a humidity tent over sprouted seedlings. A tent can

lead to excessive humidity and damping-off. Cuttings are much less susceptible to damping-off and love a humidity tent to promote rooting. (See Chapter Four to learn more about seed and cutting water requirements).

Damping-off rots the stem at the soil line. It is usually caused by soggy soil.

Control damping-off in its early stages by watering with a fungicide such as a mild bleach solution (two to five drops per gallon). Dust seeds with diatomaceous earth to prevent this disease. Damping-off usually progresses rapidly and kills the young seedling in a matter of days. Over-watering is the biggest cause of damping-off and the key to prevention. An alternative to a humidity tent is to mist cuttings with water several times daily. This practice maintains leaf moisture and high humidity.

Soil-borne Fungus

Soil-borne fungus attacks the root system. It is usually seen on the soil surface first, or growing around the roots in the soil. Soil-borne fungus normally starts from using an unsterile planting medium and improper drainage. Poor drainage keeps roots too wet, making them susceptible to fungus and rot. **Root rot** and **dry rot** (common in bulbs) are soil borne diseases that are usually promoted by poor drainage and heavy, frequent watering, especially in the late afternoon and evening. The roots or bulbs turn brown and slimy. The foliage may discolor, wilt and even die. Aphids, nematodes and other insects act as vectors to these diseases.

Prevent root and bulb rots by supplying adequate drainage and water infrequently during the morning. Crop rotation helps prevent root rot because the disease that attacks one family of plants does not affect another.

Tomatoes and peppers may suffer from **blossom-end** rot. This disease causes the flower bud or fruit to turn a dark sickly color and drop. Blossom-end rot may occur after good growing conditions followed by drought during flowering and fruit formation. It can also be caused by heavy rainfall and very humid conditions.

To prevent this type of fungus, a sterile planting medium and good drainage are essential. As explained in Chapter Three, good drainage is easily attained by having adequate drain holes and the proper soil texture.

Control soil-borne fungus by applying a biodegradable soap solution or mild bleach to the soil. Three or four applications are usually necessary. Mix at the rate of one teaspoon per gallon of water. Apply in a water solution. Make sure the soil is not over-watered and there is adequate drainage.

Foliar Fungus

Leaf and stem fungus, including leaf spot, attack foliage. They appear as dark spots just about anywhere on the foliage. These types of fungi are usually caused by using cold water when misting plants; fungus-like spots are formed as a result of temperature stress (See "About Spraying," pages 116-118). The spots often develop into a fungus. Excessive humidity (over 60 percent) is the other leading cause of fungus.

Prevention of these types of fungi attacks is easy. Spray with tepid water; have a hygrometer to measure humidity; employ a vent fan to dissipate the excess moisture. Vast quantities of water are applied to actively growing plants. They transpire the water back into the air. If this moist air is allowed to remain in the tiny grow room, it will stifle growth. A vent fan will remove it rapidly. A hygrometer may be purchased for less than $10 at nurseries and garden centers. When humidity climbs over 60 percent, many fungi have the chance to start growing. The HID lamp and ballast emit dry heat. This heat, along with a vent fan, usually provide enough humidity control to prevent fungus in an enclosed grow room. During the winter or cooler months, dry heat from the HID system normally maintains humidity and 72^0 (22^0 C) temperatures while turned on. At night, when the HID is off, the temperature drops, causing moisture condensation, which raises humidity. Check the humidity, both day and night, to see if there is a substantial variation between them. If the humidity registers above 60 percent, and fungus is a problem, turn on the vent fan at night. This will vent off all the moist air. If the temperature is a problem, use dry heat to raise the night time temperature 5^0 or 10^0 (3 to 6^0 C) below the daytime temperature. This will keep humidity more constant.

Control foliar fungus by removing all seriously damaged foliage, take all preventive measures, then spray with one of the recommended fungicides three or four times at intervals of three to five days.

Gray Mold

Gray mold (*botrytis*) is a form of fungus that is familiar to most gardeners. It is grayish or white-to-bluish-green in color, with a fuzzy, hair-like appearance. The mold can appear on just about anything in the garden, from the walls to the soils surface.

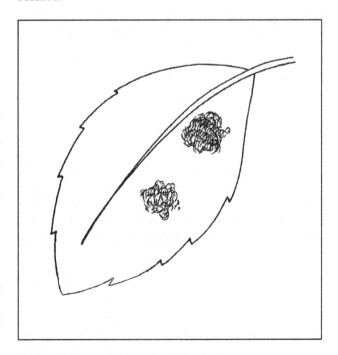

Gray mold is easily abated with fungicide sprays.

Gray mold spores are always in the air. They can be present even in the cleanest of rooms. But, as long as the proper environment is maintained, they will not grow and reproduce. Gray mold occurs in two stages: non-germinated spores that live on foliage, and germinated spores that grow and penetrate foliage tissue where the spores remain in a latent, inactive form until conditions promote disease outbreak. Gray mold loves to enter plant wounds and attack the weak plants. Spores seldom invade healthy growing tissue.

Plants have *botrytis* and have no outward sign at all. It is difficult to tell where the disease came from if there are new plants continually being introduced into the garden. Yellowing of foliage; defoliation; brown, soft areas on dark-colored petals; or white, circular spots on white to tan flowers such as roses. Spots will soon develop into the characteristic fuzzy gray mold during the reproductive stage when spores are released into the air.

Prevent gray mold with low humidity (50 percent or less). Remove any standing water, allow ample air circulation and especially ventilation. Humid geographic areas with an outside humidity over 70 percent present the biggest problem to fungus abatement. Bud mold may be triggered when dead foliage rots. When removing yellow leaves between dense buds, pluck the entire leaf so no foliage is left to rot.

Control gray mold on the soil or walls by removing it manually. Use Pinesol to wash mold from walls and containers. Do not use harsh Pinesol on plants. You must use a vegetable fungicide on plants. This kind of fungus - gray mold - thrives when the grow room is dirty or stagnant water is present.

Blight

The term blight describes many plant diseases. Signs of blight include dark blotches on foliage, slow growth sudden wilting and plant death. Most blights spread quickly through large areas of plants. Avoid blights by maintaining the proper nutrient balance in the soil and supply good drainage.

Viruses

Viruses are still a mystery. They act like living organisms in some instances and nonliving chemicals in other cases. We do know that viruses are spread by insect, minute plant, animal, and human vectors. Infected tools often carry viruses from one plant to another.

Typical symptoms of viral infection are sickly growth and low yields of flowers and fruits. In some cases, viral diseases can cause sudden wilt and death.

About Spraying

Phytotoxicity is the injury to plants. It can be caused by sprays. Symptoms include burned leaves, slow growth or sudden wilt. If you are worried about a spray damaging foliage, spray a small portion of the garden and wait a few days to see if the plants wilt or look sick.

Use chemical sprays with extreme care if at all in enclosed areas; they are more concentrated indoors than outdoors in the open air. Always wear a mask.

A large one- or two-gallon sprayer costs from $15 to $30. Nurseries and garden stores carry these sprayers. Watch for spring and fall sales to get the best deal. The sprayers have an application wand and nozzle attached to a flexible hose, which makes it very easy to spray under leaves, the most important part! Garden sprayers are also made of heavy duty materials and can take frequent use. Plastic rather than galvanized steel construction does not corrode or rust. Brass nozzle parts, with rubber gaskets are easily cleaned with a paper clip or needle.

An electric fogger works well for large jobs. The fogger has an electric blower. The spray is metered out the nozzle under pressure. It produces a fine, penetrating fog of spray. The fogger works best with insecticidal soaps, pyrethrum and fungicides. Electric forgers are used to mist commercial greenhouse plants, and are usually available through greenhouse suppliers.

One gardener uses a jackrabbit pump as a sprayer. The suction hose is placed in the nutrient solution, insecticide or fungicide, and the spray is applied with a pumping motion. The jackrabbit pump is used mainly for foliar feeding. This horticulturist notes that with daily, early morning foliar feeding, little or no problem with fungus is realized. The moisture dries before nightfall. The pump works exceptionally well for heavy organic fertilizers.

Another favorite is a small, one- or two-quart spray bottle. A Windex bottle is acceptable, but will probably clog up or break in a couple of weeks. The best bottle is found at a nursery. It will have a removable nozzle that can easily be taken apart and thoroughly cleaned if clogged. These new pump-up spray bottles are very convenient, and deliver an adjustable spray. Homemade organic teas clog most sprayers. A straight pin should be handy to clear the nozzle hole. Buy a heavy-duty spray bottle that can take a lot of use. It takes about 3/4 quart of spray to cover a 10-by-10-foot garden. That is a lot of pumping for a very small plastic spray bottle!

The small sprayers are easy to handle in the confines of a growing area and will hold enough liquid to spray the entire garden.

Always wash the bottle and pump thoroughly before and after each use. Using the same bottle for fertilizers and insecticides is okay. However, for best results: Do not mix fertilizers and insecticides or fungicides together when applying. Mixing chemicals will lessen their effectiveness. Chemicals might also be incompatible, one inhibiting the other's effects.

Mix pesticides and fungicides just before using. Fertilizer solutions can be mixed and used for several weeks afterward. When finished spraying, empty the excess spray into the toilet. Spray residues have a tendency to build up in a partially clean bottle. Fresh water is the only liquid to leave in the spray bottle overnight.

Always spray early in the day. The moist spray needs a chance to be absorbed and dry out. If sprayed just a few hours before nightfall, moisture left overnight on foliage could cause fungus or water spots.

Always use tepid or room-temperature water. Water too hot or cold shocks plants and will cause water spots on leaves. Plants are able to absorb and process tepid water more rapidly.

Before spraying fungicides and pesticides, make sure the plants are well watered. With more water in the system, a plant suffers less shock from the spray. When foliar feeding the garden with a soluble fertilizer, just the opposite is true. Plants will absorb the soluble nutrients more rapidly when there is less moisture in the plant and soil. This is not a reason to let plants dry out!

When mixing, read the entire label and follow directions to the letter. Mix wettable powders and soluble crystals in a little hot water to make sure they get dissolved before adding the balance of the tepid water.

Novice gardeners who have never sprayed before may want to talk the process over with their nurseryperson before starting.

Always spray the entire plant, both sides of the leaves, stems, soil and pot. When spraying heavily, be careful with new tender growing shoots; they are easily burned by harsh sprays.

Have an accurate measuring cup and spoon that are used *only* for the indoor garden. Keep them clean. If the spray is too heavy (easy to do when mixing small amounts) it will not kill any more insects any more dead; it will burn plants. Extreme precision should be exercised when mixing small quantities. A few drops could make the spray too potent and burn tender plants.

Spraying could promote mold, once flower buds form and growth becomes dense. The moisture is trapped in the dense foliage of the flower cluster. If this water is allowed to remain in the flower top a day or longer, the mold will find a new home.

Always rinse plants with tepid water one or two days after spraying. The water should actually drip from the leaves to have a cleansing effect. Misting plants heavily washes away all the stomata-clogging film and residue left from sprays. Fertilizer left on leaves is dissolved and absorbed by the rinse. Make sure both sides of the leaves are thoroughly rinsed.

Spray plants that have fragile foliage with wettable powders rather than liquid concentrates. Inert diluents used in many liquid concentrate wilts frail plants. A harmless visible white residue results from the powder spray, but not from the liquid concentrates. A wetting or spreader-sticker is often required with wettable powders, and continuous agitation of the solution is necessary. This heavy, powdery film could require two or three rinses to wash it off foliage.

Always rinse vegetables several times with a fresh-water spray a week before harvesting.

Sprays are beneficial if not overdone. Every time a plant is sprayed with a fungicide or insecticide, the stomata are clogged and growth slows. Rinsing off spray helps, but if sprays are used over and over, the garden will be slow-growing.

Health concious gardeners use insecticides and fungicides that are *contact* sprays that may be used on edible fruits and vegetables. Read the entire label to find the toxic or active life of the spray. Wait a few more days than the label recommends and thoroughly wash all vegetables before eating if you plan to use chemicals. Even ornamentals should be sprayed sparingly in the indoor environment. Toxic sprays tend to linger much longer indoors. The toxic life or chemicals is normally twice as long indoors because sunlight and weathering breaks down many chemicals.

Organic or natural based sprays are also toxic and should be used sparingly. However, sprays such as pyrethrum and insecticidal soaps are not harmful to humans and animals. Most indoor gardeners prefer to use the natural sprays that are safe.

Use a respirator or face mask when spraying, especially if using an aerosol/fogger. Spray residues remain very concentrated in the enclosed grow room. This makes it easy for even the safest spray to be irritating if inhaled for long.

CAUTION! Raise HID lamp out of the way, so mist from spray will not touch the bulb. Temperature stress, resulting from the relatively cold water hitting the hot bulb, may cause it to implode. This could not only startle you, but could burn eyes and skin. If the bulb breaks, turn off the system immediately!

SECTION II
STAGES of GROWTH

The Seed and Seedling

Vegetative Growth

Transplanting

Bending and Pruning

Flowering

Plant Selection Guide

Stages of Growth

Typically, an annual plant goes through three distinct stages of growth. The seedling stage lasts about a month. During this stage, the seed germinates or sprouts, establishes a root system, grows a stem and a few leaves. During vegetative growth, the plant produces much bushy green growth as well as a supporting root system. This stage may last from two months to over a year. The last stage of the life cycle comes when flowers form. If the flowers are pollinated, seeds will form.

Indoors, with artificial light, the photoperiod (the ratio of daylight to darkness) can be controlled at will. The vegetative stage may be maintained with 18-hour days and flowering induced with 12-hour days and 12 hours of uninterrupted dark nights.

Chapter Eight

The Seed and Seedling

The seed contains all the genetic characteristics of a plant. A seed is the result of sexual propagation, having genes from both male and female parents. An exception to this rule is found in hermaphrodite plants that bear both male and female flowers. The genes within a seed dictate the plant's size, disease and pest resistance, root, stem, leaf and flower production, yield, and many other variable growth traits. The genetic makeup of a seed is the single most important factor dictating how well the plant will grow under HID lamps.

A simple picture of a seed reveals an embryo, containing the genes and a supply of food, wrapped in a protective outer coating. Fresh, dry, mature seeds sprout quickly, while older seeds (one year or more) may take longer to sprout.

Plant seeds need only water, heat and air to germinate. They sprout without light in a wide range of temperatures. Seeds, properly watered, will normally germinate in 2 to 10 days, in temperatures from 70 to 90^0 F (21 to 32^0 C). The warmer it is, the faster germination takes place. Germination temperatures above 90^0 F (32^0 C) are not advised. When the seed germinates, the outside protective shell splits, and a tiny white sprout pops out. This sprout is the tap root. The seed leaves emerge from the shell as they push upward in search of light.

There are two popular ways to germinate seeds. In a warm location (70 to 90^0 F, 21 to 32^0 C) place seeds in a moist paper towel or cheesecloth, making sure they are in darkness. Keep the cloth moist, letting excess water drain away freely. The cloth will retain enough moisture to germinate the seed in a few days.

The seed contains an adequate food supply for germination, but watering with a mild mix of liquid fertilizer will hasten growth. In a humid climate, water with a mild bleach or fungicide solution (two to five drops per gallon) to prevent fungus. Once the seeds have sprouted and the white sprout is visible, plant them. Take care not to expose the tender rootlet to prolonged, intense light or wind. Plant the germinated seed in a quarter-inch to half-inch of fine planting medium with the white sprout tip (the root) pointing down.

The second popular germination and planting method is to sow the seed in a shallow planter, one- to five-gallon pot, peat pellet or rockwool cube. The planting medium is then maintained evenly moist. If the seedling is to be transplanted from the shallow planter, use a spoon to contain the frail root ball. Peat pellets or rockwool cubes may be transplanted in 2 to 3 weeks or when the roots show through the sides. Do not forget to fertilize them if they begin to yellow.

One gardener sows the seeds in a nursery flat and places it in the drawer of her heated waterbed. As soon as the seeds sprout, they are placed on top of the waterbed for a few more days to take advantage of the bottom heat. Next, they are placed into the grow room.

A moisture tent can be constructed over the seedling container. Just put plastic bag over the seeded soil. This will maintain high humidity and temperature. Usually, the seeds need only one initial watering when this method is used. Remove the bag as soon as the first sprout appears. Leaving it on will lead to damping-off or other fungus problems.

It is not necessary, but the planted seeds may be placed under the HID lamp while germinating. The lamp will add dry heat, and the soil will require more watering. Placing heat tape under or in soil will expedite germination without drying the soil out as fast.

The biggest problem most people have with germinating seeds is over-watering. The soil must be uniformly moist. A shallow flat or planter with a heat pad underneath may require daily watering, while a deep, one-gallon pot will need watering every 3 to 7 days. When the surface is dry a quarter-inch deep it is time to water. Remember there are few roots to absorb the water early in life, and they are very delicate.

It is a good idea to plant more seeds than are expected to mature for harvest. This is the best way to ensure success and a full grow room. When plants are small, they take up very little room. The HID lamp uses the same amount of electricity to grow 10 small plants as it does to grow 100. As the plants mature, the small and sick may easily be weeded out. Strong, healthy plants are transplanted to larger containers or given to friends.

When the seed sprouts, the first leaves that appear are called seed or seedling leaves. The seed leaves spread out as the stem elongates. In a few days, the first true leaves will appear. The plant is now in the seedling stage, which will last about three more weeks. During this time, a root system grows rapidly and green growth is slow. Water is critical. The new root system is very small and requires a small but constant supply of water. Too much water will drown the roots and may cause root rot or damping-off. Lack of water will cause the infant root system to dry up. As the seedlings mature, some will grow faster, be stronger and appear generally more healthy. Others will sprout slowly, be weak and leggy. If many seeds were planted, the sick and weak can be thinned out and the strong kept. This thinning process should take place around the third to fifth week of growth. Seedlings may also be transplanted easily without any damage.

Chapter Nine

Vegetative Growth

After the seedling is established, it enters the vegetative growth stage. When chlorophyll production is in full swing, the plant will produce as much vegetative or green, leafy growth as light CO_2, nutrients and water will permit. Properly maintained, many flowers and vegetables will grow from half an inch to two inches a day. If the plant is stunted now, it could take weeks to resume normal growth. A strong, unrestricted root system is essential to supply much-needed water and nutrients.

 RULE OF THUMB: Unrestricted vegetative growth is the key to a healthy harvest.

During vegetative growth, the plant's nutrient and water intake changes. Transpiration is carried on at a more rapid rate, requiring more water. High levels of nitrogen are needed; phosphorus and potassium are used at much faster rates. The larger a plant grows, the more water it uses and the faster the soil dries out. A larger root system is able to take in more water and nutrients. Strong lateral branches are produced. They will soon be filled with flower buds. The more vegetative growth, the more flowers and fruit at harvest.

Eighteen hours of halide light is conducive to vegetative growth; after that a point of diminishing returns is reached, and the light loses effectiveness. Many annual plants will remain in the vegetative growth stage more than a year (theoretically forever) as long as the 18-hour photoperiod is maintained.

Starting Cuttings

Taking cuttings or cuttings is one of the most efficient and productive means of plant propagation known today. Almost all flowers and vegetables can be reproduced or propagated sexually or asexually. Seeds are the product of sexual propagation; cuttings are the result of asexual or vegetative propagation. Taking cuttings is simply cutting some growing branch tips and rooting them. Many people have taken cuttings from a house plant such as a philodendron, ivy or coleus, and rooted them in water or sand. The rooted cutting is then placed in rich potting soil.

Identical cuttings will vary if they are grown in different climates. If the climate is poor for growth, the plant will develop poorly and be stunted. If the grow room is well cared for and has a perfect climate, strong, healthy flowers and vegetables can be harvested.

Vegetative propagation yields an exact genetic replica of the parent plant. These cuttings will all have the characteristics of the favorite parent. Fast, squat, bushy growth is at the same rate and lends itself to easy maintenance. Under HID's, cuttings grow thick, heavy flower buds and huge vegetables.

Cuttings from the same plant grow into identical adults if grown in the exact same environment. The same cuttings grown in different grow rooms will look like different plants.

Light intensity is much greater, since the cuttings do not have a chance to get too tall. Remember, the closer the light is to the entire plant and garden, the faster they grow. Lower branches, heavily shaded by upper branches and leaves, will grow slow and spindly.

Because a cutting of any age is larger than a plant grown from seed, the root system is small and compact, making cuttings well suited for containers. By the time the root system is inhibited by the container, it is time for harvest. A five- or six-month old plant, grown from seed, is easily pot-bound and stunted. This compounds any insect or nutrient disorder.

The stronger a plant and the faster it grows, the less chance it has of being affected by diseases or insects. A spider mite infestation, developed in the fifth or sixth month of a sexually propagated (seed) crop, may have to suffer through many applications until the infestation is arrested. The grow room cannot be totally cleaned and fumigated until the plants have completed flowering or producing vegetables and been harvested.

All plants may be removed for a couple of days in order to fumigate the room or paint it with antiseptic whitewash. Moving a room full of six-month old plants in 50-pound containers of soil is hard work. The plants are sick to begin with, and moving injures them. When returned to the grow room, they will take a long time to resume normal growth. On the other hand, cuttings are not in the grow room as long; the infestations have less time to launch an all-out attack or build an immunity to sprays.

Healthy cuttings taken from a proven, disease-resistant parent are the route to a bountiful harvest. An insect infestation that gets out of hand among small cuttings is easily stopped. The small cuttings are removed with little or no damage; the grow room is then fumigated.

Experiments are more easily controlled with cuttings. Since cuttings are all the same, different stimuli (fertilizer, light, bending, etc.) introduced on selected groups of cuttings and a true comparative analysis may be made.

Cuttings have some negative points. The parent plant will produce cuttings just like it. If the parent is not disease-resistant or produces poorly, cuttings also share these weaknesses. An insect or fungus infestation, left unchecked, could wipe out an entire cutting crop.

Taking cuttings from three or four different parents will help ensure a healthy garden. Clean grow rooms rarely have insect of disease problems.

Infestations are also promoted by continued use of an ineffective spray used to kill insects or fungi.

Taking cuttings is simple and easy. A consistent 100 percent survival rate may be achieved by following the simple procedures outlined in this book. The parent plant can be grown from seed or propagated by cutting. It should be at least two months old and possess all the characteristics you find desirable.

A single branch of a parent plant can be cut into several pieces. Each piece of the branch can be rooted and will turn into a plant just like the parent.

Cuttings can be taken from just about any plant, regardless of age or growth stage. Cuttings taken in the vegetative stage root quickly and grow fast. Cuttings taken from flowering plants may root a little slower.

Taking cuttings is the most traumatic experience plants experience. Cuttings go through an incredible change when growing branch tips are cut from the parent plant. Their entire chemistry changes. The stem that once grew green leaves must now grow roots in order to survive. Sprays should be avoided now, as they compound cutting stress.

Research has found that plants tend to root much better when the stems have a high carbohydrate and low nitrogen concentration. Leaching the soil with copious quantities of water washes out nutrients including nitrogen. Heavy leaching could keep soil too soggy. An alternative to leaching the soil would be to leach the leaves themselves by reverse foliar feeding. To reverse foliar feed, fill the sprayer with clean, tepid water, and mist plants heavily every morning for a week. This washes the soluble nitrogen out of foliage rapidly. The parent plant's growth slows as the nitrogen is used, giving carbohydrates a chance to accumulate. Carbohydrate content is usually highest in lower, older, more mature branches. A rigid branch that will fold over easily when bent, rather than bend, is a good sign of high carbohydrate content. Older branches low on the plant give the best results. While rooting, cuttings require a minimum of nitrogen and increased levels of phosphorus to promote root growth.

There are several products available that stimulate root growth. They are available in a liquid or powder form. Professionals prefer the liquid type (root-inducing hormones) for penetration and consistency. The powder types are avoided because they adhere inconsistently to the stem and yield a lower survival rate.

In order for a cutting to grow roots from the stem, it must change from producing stem cells, to producing undifferentiated cells, and finally producing root cells. The rooting hormone promotes the rooting process by stimulating undifferentiated growth. Substances that are known to stimulate this type of growth are: napthalenacetic acid (NAA), indolebutyric acid (IBA) and 2,4-dichlorophenoxyacetic acid (2,3 DPA). The following products have been used as rooting hormones successfully. Many of these commercial rooting hormones have one or all of the above ingredients and a fungicide to help prevent damping-off.

Dip-N-Grow
Woods Rooting Compound
Hormex
Rootone - F

> **Note**: Some of these products are not recommended for use with edible plants. Read the label carefully before deciding to use a product.

Cuttings root faster if the soil is a few degrees warmer than normal. The soil heat promotes faster chemical activity, spurring growth. For best results, the rooting cuttings' soil should be kept at 70 to 80° F (21 to 27° C). The cuttings will transpire less if the air is about 5° (3° C) cooler than the soil. Misting cuttings with water is a good way to cool foliage and lower transpiration. This helps the cuttings retain moisture that the roots do not yet supply.

 RULE OF THUMB: Take cuttings from 5 to 10 practice cuttings before making taking a large number of cuttings.

Taking Cuttings: Step-by-Step

STEP ONE: Choose a parent at least two months old and 24 inches tall. Leach the soil daily with at least 2-gallons of water per 1 gallon of soil (make sure drainage is good), or wash down leaves with a misting of warm water (reverse foliar feeding) every morning. Start seven days before taking cuttings, and leach every morning to wash out nitrogen.

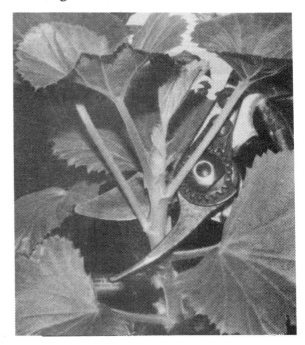

A cutting from a geranium is being taken.

STEP TWO: Choose some of the older lower branch tips as cuttings. With a sharp, clean blade, make a 45-degree cut across firm, healthy branches about an eighth- to a quarter-inch in diameter and two to eight inches in length. It is very important to keep from smashing the end of the stem when making the cut. Trim off two or three sets of leaves and buds so the stem can fit in soil. There should be at least two sets of leaves above the soil line and one or two sets of trimmed nodes below ground. When cutting, make the slice halfway between the sets of nodes. Getting too close to nodes could cause one of the remaining nodes to have mutated growth. Place the cut end in a glass of fresh, tepid water. This is will keep an air bubble from lodging in the tiny hole in the center of the stem, blocking the transpiration stream. If this hole is blocked, the new cutting will die within 24 hours. Leave the cuttings in the water overnight in subdued or no light.

STEP THREE: If possible, use peat pots or rockwool cubes, because they make maintenance easier and facilitate transplanting. Fill small containers or nursery flats with coarse, washed sand, fine vermiculite, soilless mix or, if nothing else is available, potting soil. Line the containers up and saturate them with tepid water. Use a pencil or chopstick to make a hole in the rooting medium a little larger than the stem. The hole should stop at least half an inch from the bottom of the container to allow for root growth.

Next, the cutting is dipped into diluted Hormex, a liquid root hormone, and placed in a small rockwool cubes. Roots emerge in about two weeks.

STEP FOUR: Use a root hormone. Professional nurserypeople prefer a liquid root hormone. Mix it just before using. There will be dilutions for hardwood and softwood cuttings in the mixing instructions. Use the formula for the softwood cuttings. Swirl each cutting in the hormone solution for 10 to 20 seconds. Place the cutting in the hole. Pack rooting medium gently around the

stem. Powder root hormones require no mixing. Just roll the moistened stem in the powder. When planting, take special care to keep a solid layer of hormone powder around the stem while gently packing soil into place.

STEP FIVE: Lightly water with a mild solution of B_1, until the surface is evenly moist. Water as needed.

STEP SIX: Cuttings root best with 18 hours (some gardeners swear by 24 hours) of fluorescent light. If no fluorescent lamp is available, place the cuttings three to four feet under the halide and shade them with a cloth or screen. The shade will cut light intensity and prevent excessive shock.

The photograph above shows small nobs emerging from the stem of a miniature rose that has been rooting for only ten days. Below, is a bed of carnation cuttings rooting under fluorescents.

STEP SEVEN: Place a tent over rooting cuttings to keep humidity near 80 percent. Construct the tent out of plastic bags, plastic film or glass. Remember to leave a breeze-way in the container so the little cuttings can breathe. An alternative to the humidity tent is to mist the rooting cuttings with tepid water several times daily. Either method helps retain moisture, since there are no roots to supply the leaves with water.

STEP EIGHT: The humidity tent will maintain the temperature at about 70 to 80^0 F (21 to 27^0 C). However, some plants may fall victim to damping-off if there is not an ample supply of fresh, circulating air. If more heat is needed, just moving the flat up off the floor will raise the temperature a few degrees. If the container does not raise it enough, place a heat pad, heat cable or incandescent light bulb below rooting cuttings.

STEP NINE: Some cuttings may wilt for a few days or the leaves may rot if touch moist soil. Remove rotten leaves. Cuttings should look normal by the end of a week. If cuttings are badly wilted at the end of a week, they probably won't live or are so stunted they will never catch up to the others.

STEP TEN: In one to four weeks, the cuttings should be rooted. The tips of leaves will turn yellow, and roots start growing out drain holes, and cuttings will start upward vertical growth. To check for root growth in flats or pots, carefully remove a cutting to see if it has good root development. Roots will show through the bottom and sides of peat pots and root cubes.

Transplanting

When a plant has outgrown its container, it must be transplanted into a larger pot to ensure that the roots have room for continued rapid outward growth. Inhibiting the root system will stunt plants. Some of the signs are slow, sickly growth and legginess. Branches develop with more distance between them on the main stem. It will take a long time for the plant to resume normal growth.

Transplant into the same type of soil, so there is no new soil for the roots to get used to. For cuttings rooted in vermiculite or sand, just shake away as much of the medium as possible (without damaging roots) before setting the root ball into the new soil. Novice and lazy gardeners may want to start seeds or cuttings in root cubes or peat pots. They are very easy to transplant. Just set the cube or peat pot in the soil and backfill with soil.

Next to taking cuttings, transplanting is the most traumatic experience a plant can live through. Transplanting requires special attention and manual dexterity. Tiny root hairs are very delicate and may easily be destroyed by light, air or clumsy hands. Roots grow in darkness, where their environment is rigid and secure. When roots are

taken out of contact with the soil for long, they dry up and die.

Transplanting should disturb the root system as little as possible. Vitamin B_1 is recommended to help ease transplant shock. Plants need time to get settled-in and re-establish a solid flow of fluids from the roots through the plant. They will require low levels of nitrogen and potassium, but use large quantities of phosphorus. When Up-Start is applied properly and roots are disturbed little, there will be no signs of transplant shock or wilt.

To transplant a one-inch rockwool cube, simply place it on in the pre-drilled hole in a larger cube.

After transplanting, give new transplants filtered or less intense light for a couple of days. If there is a fluorescent lamp handy, place transplants under it for a couple of days before moving them under the HID.

Transplant late in the day so transplants will have all night to recover. The secret to successful transplanting are manual dexterity, vitamin B_1, and lots of water. Water helps the soil pack around roots and keeps them from drying out. Roots need to be in constant contact with the soil so they can supply water and food to the plant. Transplants will be a little shocked no matter what is done. Think about the plant; it has changed soil and will need to settle in. During this time of settling in, photosynthesis and chlorophyll production are at a low, as is water and nutrient absorption through the roots. It needs subdued light to keep foliage growing at the same rate as roots are able to supply water and nutrients.

Plants should be as healthy as possible before suffering the trauma of transplanting. None-the-less, transplanting a sick, root-bound plant to a large container has cured more than one ailing plant.

Transplanting: Step-by-Step

In this example, we will transplant a one-month-old cutting started in a four-inch container of vermiculite into a six gallon pot.

STEP ONE: Water the four-inch cutting with half strength vitamin B_1, one or two days before transplanting.

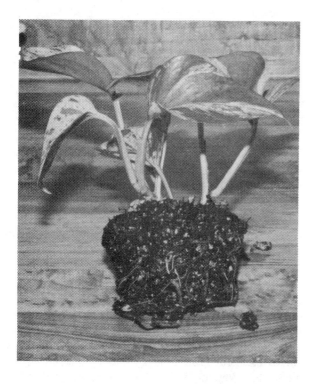

The root ball of this pothos has been carefully removed from the restricting container. It will have much more room to grow in its new container.

STEP TWO: Fill the six-gallon container with rich potting soil or soilless mix to within two inches of the top.

STEP THREE: Water soil until saturated.

STEP FOUR: Gently roll the four-inch pot between hands to break sand away from the sides of pot. Place your hand over top of container with stem between fingers; turn it upside down and let root ball slip out of pot into your hand. Take special care at this point to keep the root ball in one integral piece.

STEP FIVE: Carefully place root ball in a prepared hole in the six-gallon container. Make sure all roots are growing down.

STEP SIX: Backfill around the root ball. Gently, but firmly pack soil around the root ball.

STEP SEVEN: Water a vitamin B_1 solution, making sure soil is completely saturated, but not soggy.

STEP EIGHT: Place new transplants on the perimeter of the garden or under a screen, so light remains subdued for a couple of days. The transplants should be able to take full light within a day or two.

STEP NINE: The new, rich potting soil will supply enough nutrients for about a month. After that, supplemental fertilization will probably be necessary. Soilless mixes require balanced N-P-K fertilization a week or less after transplanting.

STEP TEN: See the chart on "Minimum Container Size" in Chapter Three, page 58.

Bending and Pruning

Bending and pruning alter the basic growth pattern of a plant. The alteration affects physical shape, liquid flow and growth hormones. Pruning strongly affects the plant, while bending has more subdued affects.

Pinching back the growing tip of this coleus will force growth on lower branches and make it more bushy.

When a branch is pruned off, two branches will grow from the nodes just below the cut. This does not mean the plant will grow twice as much; a plant can grow only so fast. A quick branch amputation is not going to make it grow faster or add any more foliage. In fact, an indoor garden is already being pushed to the limit, and trimming or cutting it will slow growth for a few days. Think about pruning before hacking away! Any time a plant is pruned, valuable foliage is being removed that could be covered with flowers in less than two months.

Pruning will make a plant grow bushier. The lower branches will develop more rapidly when the terminal bud is removed. Removing the terminal bud alters the concentration of growth-inhibiting hormones. These hormones (auxins) prevent the lateral buds from growing very fast. The further a branch is from hormones at the plant tip, the less effect the auxins have.

Always use clean instruments when pruning. A single-edged razor blade, a sharp pair of pruners or a pair of scissors, all work well. Do not use indoor pruners on anything but the indoor garden. If using pruners outdoors, they will have everything from aphids to dog dung on them. If using outdoor clippers, dip the blades into rubbing alcohol to sterilize them before use.

Pinching back branches will diffuse floral hormones, making the plant bushier. Pruning the plant when it is one or two months old and again a month later will make it bushier. Continual

pruning will keep it in a solid hedge-like shape. Some gardeners prune plants into ornamental shape.

This tomato has been pruned to four main branches.

Another pruning technique removes all but four main branches. This method is commonly used with tomatoes. The central growing tip is removed and the four branches are left intact. This concentrates the floral hormones in the four main branches.

Note: Only complete branches are pruned; leaves are left alone!

The idea behind this principle is that if there are fewer branches, they will be stronger, bearing more and heavier flowers and fruit. The seedling or cutting is generally 1- to 3-months old when the four main branches are selected. The branches selected are usually the strongest.

Pruning all the branches is not advised. It shocks the plant too much. Pruning the tall branches that get in the way and rob light from the rest of the garden works well. However, if taking cuttings from a parent, you may want to sacrifice its well-being for more cuttings. Remember, if it is pruned down to stubby branches, it could take it a month to resume normal growth.

Pruning too much over a period of time may alter the hormonal balance so much that the plant produces spindly growth. If a plant must be pruned heavily for cuttings, it is usually best to prune it right down to a few leafy growing tips on the trunk or main stem and let it grow back from there.

All leaves are to be left alone! Somehow a rumor started about how removing large shade leaves would supply more light to smaller growing tips, making them grow faster. This is bad gardening! A plant needs all the leaves it can get to produce the maximum amount of chlorophyll. Removing leaves slows chlorophyll production and stunts growth. Removing the leaves stresses the plant. Stress inhibits growth, especially during vegetative growth. Only leaves that are clearly dead, insect- or fungus-infected, should be removed. Leaf removal is not pruning, it is hacking up a normally healthy plant.

Pruning or trimming off lower branches that have spindly, sickly growth, is acceptable. When pruning, cut off the entire branch. Pruning the lower branches has a minimal effect on floral hormone concentration.

Chapter Ten

Flowering

In order for a plant to complete its annual life cycle successfully, it must first flower. Dioecious plants are either male (pollen producing) or female (ovule producing). Hermaphrodite plants are bisexual, with both male and female flowers on the same plant.

One of the many tiny grains of pollen from the male (staminate) flower pod lands on a pistil of the female (pistillate) flower. Each calyx harbors an ovule and a protruding set of pistils. Actual fertilization takes place when the grain of male pollen slides down the pistil and unites with the female ovule, deep within the calyx. Once fertilization takes place, pistils turn brown and a seed will form within the calyx or seed bract. Seeds are the result of this sexual propagation and contain genetic characteristics of both parents.

Long-day plants

In nature, annual plants life cycle comes to an end in the fall, after the long, hot, days of summer. The long nights and short days of autumn signal short-day plants to start the flowering stage. Growth patterns and chemistry change: Stems elongate, flower formation is rapid at first, then slows. All this causes new nutrient needs. Attention is now focused on flower production, rather than on vegetative growth. Production of chlorophyll, requiring much nitrogen, slows. Phosphorus uptake increases to promote floral formation. Light needs change as well. During autumn, in most climates, the sun takes on a slightly reddish appearance, emitting a light that is a more red than white. Growth and floral hormones are stimulated by this red or harvest sun.

Chrysanthemums are short-day plants that bloom under 12 hours of light and 12 hours of total darkness.

The harvest sun phenomenon is not fully understood. However, experiments have proved that by increasing the amount of red light during flowering, floral hormones are stimulated and flower yield increases substantially.

Indoors, flowering may be induced in short-day plants just as it is in nature, by shortening the photoperiod from 18 to 12 hours. Once the days are changed to 12 hours, flowers should be clearly visible within one to three weeks. In fact, some gardeners have two grow rooms: a vegetative grow room with one metal halide that supplies 18 hours of light. The other room for growing short-day plants that has both a halide and HP sodium that is on for 12 hours a day.

Using this combination of rooms and lamps, the electricity bill remains relatively low and the horticulturist has the luxury of having both summer and fall every day of the year!

The additional stimulation of a red or harvest sun may be simulated by an HP sodium lamp (the phosphor-coated halide also emits a little more red than the clear halide). The HP sodium may increase flower production 20 to 50 percent over a halide.

The harvest sun is simulated one of three ways: (1) Adding an HP sodium lamp to a grow room already containing a metal halide. This more than doubles the available light, especially in the red end of the spectrum. The halide maintains blues in the spectrum necessary for continued chlorophyll production. (2) Replacing the halide with an HP sodium. This increases the reds, but cuts the blues. A result of this practice has been more yellowing of vegetative leaves, due to lack of chlorophyll production and more stem elongation than if the halide were present. (3) Adding or changing to a phosphor-coated halide. Not only are these halides easier on the eyes, their coating makes them produce a little bit more red in their spectrum, thus promoting flowering.

Water needs of a flowering plant are somewhat less than in the vegetative stage. Adequate water during flowering is important to carry on the plant's chemistry. Withholding water to stress a plant will actually stunt growth and the yield will be less.

Hermaphrodites

A hermaphrodite is a plant that has both male and female flowers on the same plant. The majority of plants fall into this category.

Indoors, the outdoor environment is manufactured and the normal life cycle of any plant can be altered. Creating summer in December, taking cuttings, prolonging the life cycle and leaching the soil - all the wonderful things we are able to do indoors, mixes up even the strongest plant somewhat. When this stress is coupled with weak seeds, the outcome is uncertain. High humidity, over-pruning and old age seem to promote hermaphrodites more than other environmental factors. In short, if a plant starts to go sour and you do not know the reason why, it could be because it was stressed too much.

Seed Crops

Seed crops are harvested when the seeds are mature. Often seeds may actually split open their containing calyx or seed pod. The flower grows many ready, receptive calyxes until pollination occurs. Seeds are normally mature within six to eight weeks. Watch out for fungus that might attack the weakening flower and cache of ripe seeds.

When seeds are mature, remove them from the pods and store them in a cool, *dry* place. The seeds are viable and ready for planting as soon as they are harvested, but they may grow sickly plants. Let the seeds dry out a few months before planting. Dry seeds will produce much healthier plants and the germination rate will be higher.

Chapter Eleven

Plant Selection Guide

Plant Selection Guide

African violets, begonias and impatiens flower constantly under lights. Begonias of all types, ferns, oxalis, geraniums, annuals, small shrubs and trees such as jasmine, gardenia, crape myrtle, dwarf lantana and dwarf pomegranate, citrus and figs all grow well under HID's.

Cacti and succulents - jade, miniature crassulas, Christmas, Easter and Thanksgiving cactus, etc. - are probably the easiest to care for under lights. They require a minimum of care and infrequent watering, but lots of light.

African Violets, parent plants and cuttings of this short-day plant are given 18 hours of light a day at a level of 6,000 mWm^2. Flowering is induced with a short 12 to 14-hour photoperiod.

Azalea cuttings propagated under a light level of 6,000 mWm^2, 18 hours a day grow fast and uniform. Flowers are effectively forced by supplying 3,000 mWm$_{s2}$ for 16 hours a day.

Begonias: Supplemental lighting promotes cuttings to form on the varieties Rieger, Elatior and Lorraine when natural light is lacking. A light level of 6,000 mWm^2 is the norm. Use 6,000 mWm^2 18 hours a day to nurture young seedlings and to speed flowering. Rooting is stimulated in begonia cuttings by artificial light.

Bromeliads: A light level of 6,000 mWm^2 18 hours a day is used to promote stronger growth and the development of seedlings and young plants. On larger bromeliads, supplemental lighting is normally used to help stimulate floral formation.

A light level of 4,500 mWm^2 for 24 hours a day is used to stimulate flowering. Many times other flower-inducing means are combined with lighting to hasten blooming.

Cacti: In winter when the days are short, cacti greatly benefit from intense supplemental light. A lighting level of 9,000 mWm^2 for 18 hours a day will produce phenomenal results in seedlings, cuttings and adult cacti. Some varieties of cactus respond more favorably to 24 hours of light.

Calceolaria: Early flowering is achieved by applying supplemental lighting (3,000 mWm^2) for 24 hours a day from bud induction until flowering. Maintain the temperature between 60 and 65 degrees for maximum productivity.

Carnations, like chrysanthemums, are propagated very successfully by using a parent plant and supplemental light. In fact, side shoots from cut flowers make excellent cuttings. Cuttings are taken and given 16 hours of light (6,000 mWm^2). Excessive flowering may occur if more than 16 hours of light per day is permitted. The carnation is a long-day plant, it is possible to light it 24 hours a day to grow more and more profuse flowers. However, after 18 hours of light a day, the extra light produces a minimum of growth.

This high quality light meter measures the exact amount of light that is available to plants.

Chrysanthemums are one of the most responsive flowers to supplemental light in all stages of life. In winter parent plants are given 9,000 mWm^2, 20 hours a day. Given lighting during the first month of vegetative growth increases bud count and foliage production. Being a short-day plant, the chrysanthemum requires 20 hours of light a day during the first month of vegetative growth and 12 hours of light (4,500 mWm^2 and 12 hours of uninterrupted darkness to flower properly.

Cucumber seedlings grow exceptionally well under HID lights. Give young seedlings a light level of 4500 mWm² for the first 10 days of growth for 24 hours a day. After this, shorten the photoperiod to 16 hours per day, and increase the light level to 6000 mWm².

Cyclamen seedlings given supplemental lighting (6,000 mWm²) have more uniform growth and less damping off. The young plants are given 18 hours of light a day.

Geraniums and pelargoniums propagated by seed or from cuttings greatly benefit from supplemental light. Parent plants are given 18 hours of light at a level of 6,000 mWm² to increase cutting production. The cuttings are given less light but for the same 18 hours a day. Geraniums are a short-day plant and flower with shorter days or colder temperatures.

F¹ hybrid seed-propagated geraniums can be given 24 hours of light a day at a level of 6,000 mWm² from the beginning of life. These F¹ hybrids do not need short days for flower induction.

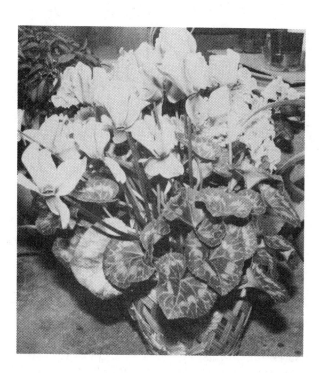

This cyclamen has been blooming for over three months and continues to bloom.

Gloxinas are given a light level of 6000 mWm² 18 hours a day to enhance growth and development of seedlings and young plants. Give potted gloxinas a light level of 4500 mWm² to promote large healthy flowers.

Kalanchoe parent plants are given 18 hours of light a day to prevent flowering of this long-day plant. Normally propagated vegetatively, cuttings are given 18 to 24 hours of light at a level of 6,000 mWm². Flowering is induced by giving the plants an equal 12 hours of light and 12 hours of darkness.

Lettuce is lighted at a level of 6000 mWm² during its entire life. If given a higher level of light, lettuce might bolt.

Transplanted on the same day, the small stone plant (lithops) on the left was in a dim corner of the grow room. The large stone plant on the right received intense halide light.

Orchids: The blooms and overall growth of many varieties of orchids are greatly enhanced by supplemental lighting during the winter. See: special section below on light requirements of orchids.

Roses love light. Miniature roses grow incredibly well under HID light. Levels of 6,000 mWm², 24 hours per day will greatly increase flower yield, size and quality. Supplemental CO_2 really boost growth of these super-productive roses.

Snapdragons are a favorite fall and early spring flower. There are two genetically different types of snapdragons; short-day, referred to as Group I or II, or "winter flowering," and long-day, referred to as Group III or IV, or "summer flowering." When setting this plant out for early spring blooms, give seedlings supplementary lighting at a level of 9,000 mWm² so that a day length of 16 hours is reached. This will speed flowering by about four weeks. In fact, even better results can be achieved by giving long-day plants 24 hours of light (4,500 mWm^2) throughout their life. Short day snapdragons should receive short 12 hour days after they are about two months old for maximum blooming potential.

Tomatoes, peppers and eggplants flourish under HID light. The more light these plants are given the bigger they grow and the more fruit they produce. Give these plants 9000 mWm^2 as soon the first true leaves appear and maintain the light level throughout their entire life.

Orchid Culture Under Lights

Light requirements for orchids fall into three categories.

High: 3000 foot-candles or more, which is equivalent to the amount of light available to plants growing in the middle of a sunny field.

Medium: 1500-3000 foot-candles, which is similar to the amount of light received by lightly shaded plants.

Low: under 1500 foot-candles, for plants that grow deep beneath the canopy of the forest.

This entire crop was propagated asexually.

Temperature requirements are divided into three groups:

Warm: (70 to 75^0 F, 21 to 24^0 C) day, (60 to 65^0 F, 15 to 18^0 C) night; similar to the climate of a seacoast or swampy lowland.

Medium: (65 to 70^0 F, 18 to 21^0 C) day, (55 to 60^0 F, 13 to 15^0 C) night; similar to rolling forests and fields.

Cool: (60 to 65^0 F, 15 to 18^0 C) day, (50 to 55^0, 10 to 13^0 C) night; similar to high mountainous regions.

Orchids can be referred to as being high light, cool-air plants. The cymbidium is a good example of this type of orchid. The Phalaenopsis genus is a low-light, warm-air orchid.

All plants may be divided into two groups: species and hybrid. Hybridization often eliminates many of the natural limitations imposed by the original climatic requirements of an orchid. For example, if you breed a high-light, warm-air species with a medium-light, medium-temperature species, the result is a hybrid that grows well in either category.

Glossary

This Glossary contains many very simple and some not so simple words in the context of their usage in this book. Many examples are given to promote good indoor horticultural practices.

Alternating Current (AC) - an electric current that reverses its direction at regularly occurring intervals. Homes have AC.

Acid - a sour substance: An acid or sour soil has a low pH.

Adobe - heavy clay soil, not suitable for container gardening

Aeration - supplying soil and roots with air or oxygen

Aeroponics - growing plants by misting roots suspended in air

Aggregate - medium, usually gravel, that is all nearly the same size, and used for the inert hydroponic medium.

Alkaline - refers to soil with a high pH: Any pH over 7 is considered alkaline.

All-purpose (General-purpose) fertilizer - A balanced blend of N-P-K: all purpose fertilizer is used by most growers in the vegetative growth stage.

Amendment - changing soil texture by adding organic or mineral substances

Ampere (amp) - the unit used to measure the strength of an electric current: A 20-amp circuit is overloaded when drawing more than 17 amps.

Annual - a plant that normally completes its entire life cycle in one year or less: Marigolds and tomatoes are examples of annual plants.

Arc - luminous discharge of electricity (light) between two electrodes.

Arc tube - container for luminous gases; also houses the arc.

Auxin - classification of plant hormones: Auxins are responsible for foliage and root elongation.

Bacteria - very small, one-celled organisms that have no chlorophyll.

Beneficial insect - a good insect that eats bad flower and vegetable-munching insects.

Biodegradable - able to decompose or break down through natural bacterial action: Substances made of organic matter are biodegradable.

Bleach - Ordinary laundry bleach is used in a mild water solution as a soil fungicide.

Bolt - term used to describe a plant that has run to seed prematurely.

Bonsai - a very short or dwarfed plant.

Breaker box - electrical circuit box having on/off switches rather than fuses.

Breathe - Roots draw in or breathe oxygen, stomata draw in or breathe CO_2.

Bud blight - a withering condition that attacks flower buds.

Buffering - the ability of a substance to reduce shock and cushion against pH fluctuations. Many fertilizers contain buffering agents.

Bulb - 1. the outer glass envelope or jacket that protects the arc tube of an HID lamp 2. clove or bulb of garlic.

Calyx - the pod harboring female ovule and two protruding pistils, seed pod.

Carbon dioxide (CO_2) - a colorless, odorless, tasteless gas in the air necessary for plant life.

Carbohydrate - neutral compound of carbon, hydrogen and oxygen: Sugar, starch and cellulose are carbohydrates.

Caustic - capable of destroying, killing or eating away by chemical activity

Cell - the base structural unit that plants are made of: Cells contain a nucleus, membrane, and chloroplasts.

Cellulose - a complex carbohydrate that stiffens a plant: Tough stems contain stiff cellulose.

CFM - Cubic feet per minute.

Chelate - combining nutrients in an atomic ring that is easy for plants to absorb.

Chlorophyll - the green photosynthetic matter of plants: Chlorophyll is found in the chloroplasts of a cell.

Chlorine - chemical used to purify water.

Chloroplast - containing chlorophyll

Chlorosis - the condition of a sick plant with yellowing leaves due to inadequate formation of chlorophyll: Chlorosis is caused by a nutrient deficiency, usually iron or imbalanced pH.

Circuit - a circular route traveled by electricity.

Clay - soil made of very fine organic and mineral particles: Clay is not suitable for container gardening.

Climate - the average condition of the weather in a grow room or outdoors.

Color spectrum - the band of colors (measured in nm) emitted by a light source.

Color tracer - a coloring agent that is added to many commercial fertilizers so the horticulturist knows there is fertilizer in the solution. Peters has a blue color tracer.

Compaction - soil condition that results from tightly packed soil: Compacted soil allows for only marginal aeration and root penetration.

Companion planting - planting garlic, marigolds, etc. along with other plants to discourage insect infestations.

Compost - a mixture of decayed organic matter, high in nutrients: Compost must be at least one year old. When too young, decomposition uses nitrogen; after sufficient decomposition, compost releases nitrogen.

Core - the transformer in the ballast is referred to as a core.

Cotyledon - seed leaves, first leaves that appear on a plant.

Cross-pollinate - pollinate two plants having different ancestry.

Cubic foot - volume measurement in feet: Width times length times height equals cubic feet.

Cutting - 1. growing tip cut from a parent plant for asexual propagation 2. clone

Damping-off - fungus disease that attacks young seedlings and cuttings causing stem to rot at base: Over-watering is the main cause of damping-off.

Direct Current (DC) - an electric current that flows in only one direction

Deplete - exhaust soil of nutrients, making in infertile: Once a soil is used it is depleted

Desiccate - cause to dry up. Safer's Insecticidal Soap desiccates its victims.

Detergent - liquid soap concentrate used as a: 1. wetting agent for sprays and water 2. pesticide. Note: Detergent must be totally organic to be safe for plants.

Dioecious - having distinct male and female flowers.

Dome - the part of the HID outer bulb opposite the neck and threads.

Dome support - the spring-like brackets that mount the arc tube within the outer envelope.

Drainage - way to empty soil of excess water: with good drainage, water passes through soil evenly, promoting plant growth; with bad drainage water stands in soil, drowning roots.

Dripline - a line around a plant directly under its outermost branch tips: Roots seldom grow beyond the drip line.

Drip system - a very efficient watering system that employs a main hose with small water emitters. Water is metered out of the emitters, one drop at a time.

Dry ice - a cold, white substance formed when CO_2 is compressed and cooled: Dry ice changes into CO_2 gas at room temperatures.

Dry well - drain hole, filled with rocks.

Electrode - a conductor used to establish electrical arc or contact with non-metallic part of circuit.

Elongate - grow in length.

Envelope - outer protective bulb or jacket of a lamp.

Equinox - the point at which the sun crosses the equator and day and night are each 12 hours long: The equinox happens twice a year.

Extension cord - extra electrical cord that must be 14-gauge or larger (i.e. 12- or 10-gauge).

Feed - fertilize.

Female - pistillate, ovule, seed-producing.

Fertilizer burn - over-fertilization: First leaf tips burn (turn brown) then leaves curl.

Fixture - electrical fitting used to hold electric components.

Flat - shallow (three-inch) deep container, often 18 by 24 inches with good drainage, used to start seedlings or cuttings.

Flat white - very reflective, whitest white paint available.

Fluorescent lamp - electric lamp using a tube coated with fluorescent material, which has low lumen and heat output: A fluorescent lamp is excellent for rooting cuttings.

Foliage - the leaves, or more generally, the green part of a plant

Foliar feeding - misting fertilizer solution which is absorbed by the foliage.

Fritted - fused or embedded in glass. Fritted trace elements (FTE) are long-lasting and do not leach out easily.

Fungicide - a product that destroys or inhibits fungus.

Fungistat - a product that inhibits fungus keeping it in check.

Fungus - a lower plant lacking chlorophyll which may attack green plants: Mold, rust, mildew, mushrooms and bacteria are fungi.

Fuse - electrical safety device consisting of a metal that MELTS and interrupts the circuit when circuit is overloaded.

Fuse box - box containing fuses that control electric circuits.

GPM - Gallons per minute

General purpose fertilizer - See: ALL-PURPOSE FERTILIZER.

Gene - part of a chromosome that influences the development and potency of a plant: Genes are inherited through sexual propagation.

Genetic make-up - the genes inherited from parent plants: Genetic make-up is the most important factor dictating vigor and potency.

Halide - binary compound of a halogen(s) with an electropositive element(s).

Halogen - any of the elements fluorine, chlorine, bromine, iodine and astatine existing in a free state: Halogens are in the arc tube of a halide lamp.

Hermaphrodite - one plant having both male and female flowers: The breeding of hermaphrodites is hard to control.

Hertz (Hz) - a unit of a frequency that cycles one time each second: A home with a 60 hertz AC current cycles 60 times per second.

HID - High Intensity Discharge.

Honeydew - a sticky, honey-like substance secreted onto foliage by aphids, scale and mealy bugs.

Hood - reflective cover of a HID lamp: A large, white HOOD is very reflective.

HOR - The abbreviation stamped on some HID bulbs meaning they may be burned in a horizontal position.

Horizontal - parallel to the horizon, ground or floor.

Hormone - chemical substance that controls the growth and development of a plant. Root-inducing hormones help cuttings root.

Hose bib - water outlet containing an on/off valve.

Humidity (relative) - ratio between the amount of moisture in the air and the greatest amount of moisture the air could hold at the same temperature.

Humus - dark, fertile, partially decomposed plant or animal matter: Humus forms the organic portion of the soil.

Hybrid - an offspring from two plants of different breeds, variety or genetic make-up.

Hydrated lime - instantly soluble lime, used to raise or lower pH.

Hydrogen - light, colorless, odorless gas: Hydrogen combines with OXYGEN to form water.

Hygrometer - instrument for measuring relative humidity in the atmosphere: A hygrometer will save time, frustration and money.

Inbred - (true breed) offspring of plants of the same breed or ancestry.

Inert - chemically non-reactive: Inert growing mediums make it easy to control the chemistry of the nutrient solution.

Intensity - the magnitude of light energy per unit: Intensity diminishes the farther away from the source.

Jacket - protective outer bulb or envelope of lamp.

Jiffy 7 pellet - compressed peat moss wrapped in an expandable plastic casing: When moistened, a Jiffy 7 pellet expands into a small pot that is used to start seeds or cuttings.

Kilowatt-hour - measure of electricity used per hour: A 1000-watt HID uses one kilowatt per hour. Lacewing insect that preys on

Leach - dissolve or wash out soluble components of soil by heavy watering.

Leader - See MERISTEM.

Leaf curl - leaf malformation due to over-watering, over fertilization, lack of magnesium, insect or fungus damage or negative tropism.

Leaflet - small immature leaf.

Leggy - abnormally tall, with sparse foliage: Legginess of a plant is usually caused by lack of light.

Life cycle - a series of growth stages through which plant must pass in its natural lifetime: The stages for an annual plant are seed, seedling, vegetative and floral.

Light mover - a device that moves a lamp back and forth across the ceiling of a grow room to provide more even distribution of light.

Lime - used in the form of DOLOMITE or HYDRATED LIME to raise and stabilize soil pH.

Litmus paper - chemically sensitive paper used for testing pH.

Loam - organic soil mixture of crumbly clay, silt and sand.

Lumen - measurement of light output: One lumen is equal to the amount of light emitted by one candle that falls on one square foot of surface located one foot away from one candle.

Macro-nutrient - one or all of the primary nutrients N-P-k or the secondary nutrients magnesium and calcium.

Mean - average throughout life: HID's are rated in mean lumens.

Meristem - tip of plant growth, branch tip.

Micro-nutrients - also referred to as TRACE ELEMENTS, including S, Fe, Mn, B, Mb, An and Cu.

Millimeter - thousandth of a meter; approximately .04 inch.

Moisture meter - a fantastic electronic device that measures the exact moisture content of soil at any given point.

Monochromatic - producing only one color: LP sodium lamps are monochromatic.

Mulch - a protective covering of organic compost, old leaves, etc.: Indoors, mulch keeps soil too moist, and possible fungus could result.

Nanometer - .000001 meter, nm is used as a scale to measure electromagnetic wave lengths of light: Color and light spectrums are expressed in namometers (nm).

Necrosis - localized death of a plant part.

Neck - tubular glass end of the HID bulb, attached to the threads.

Nutrient - plant food, essential elements N-P-K, secondary and trace elements fundamental to plant life.

Ohm's Power Law - a law that expresses the strength of an electric current: Volts times Amperes equals watts.

Organic - made of, derived from or related to living organisms.

Outbred - see hybrid.

Overload - load to excess: A 20-amp circuit drawing 17 amps is overloaded.

Ovule - a plant's egg; found within the calyx, it contains all the female genes: When fertilized, an ovule will grow into a seed.

Oxygen - tasteless, colorless element, necessary in soil to sustain plant life.

Parasite - organism that lives on or in another host organism: Fungus is a parasite.

Peat - partially decomposed vegetation (usually moss) with slow decay due to extreme moisture and cold.

Perennial - a plant, such as a tree or shrub, that completes its life cycle over several years.

pH - a scale from 1 to 14 that measures the acid-to-alkaline balance a growing medium (or anything): In general plants grow best in a range of 6 to 6.8 pH.

pH tester - electronic instrument or chemical used to find where soil or water is on the pH scale.

Phosphor coating - internal bulb coating that diffuses light and is responsible for various color outputs.

Photoperiod - the relationship between the length of light and dark in a 24-hour period.

Photosynthesis - the building of chemical compounds (carbohydrates) from light energy, water and CO_2.

Phototropism - the specific movement of a plant part toward a light source.

Pigment - The substance in paint or anything that absorbs light, producing (reflecting) the same color as the pigment.

Pollen - fine, yellow, dust-like microspores containing male genes.

Pod seed - a dry calyx containing a mature or maturing seed.

Pot-bound - bound, stifled or inhibited from normal growth, by the confines of a container: Root system become pot-bound.

Power surge - interruption or change in flow of electricity.

Primary nutrients - N-P-K.

Propagate - 1. Sexual - produce a seed by breeding different male and a female flowers 2. Asexual - to produce a plant by taking cuttings.

Prune - alter the shape and growth pattern of a plant by cutting stems and shoots.

PVC pipe - plastic (polyvinyl chloride) pipe that is easy to work with, readily available and used to pipe water into a grow room or make a watering wand.

Pyrethrum - natural insecticide made from the blossoms of various chrysanthemums: Raids' Pyrethrum is the most effective natural spider mite exterminator.

Rejuvenate - Restore youth: A mature plant, having completed its life cycle (flowering), may be stimulated by a new 18 hour photoperiod, to rejuvenate or produce new vegetative growth.

Root-bound - see POT BOUND.

Salt - crystalline compound that results from improper pH or toxic buildup of fertilizer. Salt will burn plants, preventing them from absorbing nutrients.

Secondary nutrients - calcium (Ca) and magnesium (Mg).

Short circuit - condition that results when wires cross and form a circuit. A short circuit will blow fuses.

Socket - threaded, wired holder for a bulb.

Soluble - able to be dissolved in water.

Spore - seed-like offspring of a fungus.

Sprout - 1. a recently germinated seed 2. small new growth of leaf or stem.

Square feet (sq. ft.) - length (in feet) times width equals square feet.

Staminate - male, pollen-producing.

Starch - complex carbohydrate: Starch is manufactured and stored food.

Sterilize - make sterile (super-clean) by removing dirt, germs and bacteria.

Stroboscopic effect - a quick pulsating or flashing of a lamp.

Stress - a physical or chemical factor that causes extra exertion by plants: A stressed plant will not grow as well as a non-stressed plant.

Stomata - small mouth-like or nose-like openings (pores) on leaf underside, responsible for transpiration and many other life functions: The millions of stomata, must be kept very clean to function properly.

Sugar - food product of a plant.

Super-bloom - a common name for fertilizer high in phosphorus that promotes flower formation and growth

Synthesis - production of a substance, such as chlorophyll, by uniting light energy and elements or chemical compounds.

Sump - reservoir or receptacle that serves as a drain or holder for hydroponic nutrient solutions.

Tap root - the main or primary root that grows from the seed: Lateral roots will branch off the tap root.

Teflon tape - tape that is extremely useful to help seal all kinds of pipe joints. I like Teflon tape better than putty.

Tepid - warm 70 to 80^0 F (21 to 27^0 C). Always use tepid water around plants to facilitate chemical processes and ease shock.

Terminal bud - bud at the growing end of the main stem.

Thin - cull or weed out weak, slow growing seedlings.

Toxic life - the amount of time a pesticide or fungicide remains active or live.

Transformer - a devise in the ballast that transforms electric current from one voltage to another.

Transpire - give off water vapor and by products via the stomata.

Trellis - frame of small boards (lattice) that trains or supports plants.

True breed - see INBRED.

Tungsten - a heavy, hard metal with a high melting point which conducts electricity well: Tungsten is used for a filament in tungsten halogen lamps.

Ultraviolet - light with very short wave lengths, out of the visible spectrum.

Variety - strain, phenotype (see strain).

Vent - opening such as a window or door that allows the circulation of fresh air.

Ventilation - circulation of fresh air, fundamental to healthy indoor garden. An exhaust fan creates excellent ventilation.

Vertical - up and down; perpendicular to the horizontal.

Wetting agent - compound that reduces the droplet size and lowers the surface tension of the water, making it wetter. Liquid concentrate dish soap is a good wetting agent if it is biodegradable.

Wick - part of a passive hydroponic system using a wick suspended in the nutrient solution, the nutrients pass up the wick and are absorbed by the medium and roots.

Index

Index

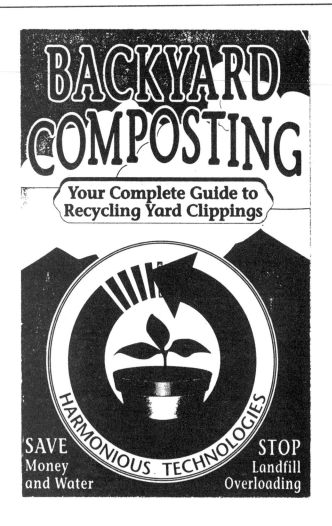

"Backyard composting is one of the hottest green trends of the 90's."
- Los Angeles Times, June 6, 1991

"Backyard Composting - An ideal resource for recyclers."
David Loveland, Executive Director
National Recycling Coalition

96 pages

5 1/2" x 8 1/2"

$6.95

Order direct from Publisher's Distribution Service

** 1-800-345-0096 **

An Easy step-by-step guide to successful composting.

Spend five minutes a week and:

> Save $$ by fertilizing and watering less
> Grow healthier and stronger plants
> Stop overloading our landfills

Learn how easy it is to:

START. Discusses all types of composting bins and accessories. Includes instructions to build a composting bin from scrap materials.

MAINTAIN. Includes easy-to-make "hot recipes', time-saving tips and a troubleshooting chart.

USE. Compost feeds your soil and reduces plant water requirements. Save money by making your own free fertilizer at home.

Harmonious Technologies specializes in Earth-friendly products and services. We help cities develop backyard composting programs.

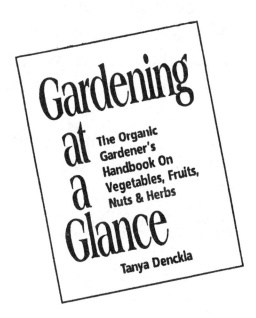

"This book is a masterpiece of detailed gardening information. You may never have to ask another question." - *Bob Thompson, host of the PBS Victory Garden, author*

272 pages

8 1/2 x 11"

$22.95

Order direct from Publisher's Distribution Service

** 1-800-345-0096 **

HERE'S WHY *GARDENING AT A GLANCE* IS FOR EVERY GARDENER...

This book is a time-saving tool. Do you have to search through 20 different books for that one piece of information on tomatoes? Whether expert or beginner, large or small scale, you'll find this condensed reference answers your questions. On one page. Spacing, starting dates, planting depth, pH, all these are at your fingertips.

The organization is gardener-friendly. Each plant is presented on one page. Opposite are varieties--heirloom, specialty, regional, disease-resistant--all selected specifically for the organic gardener. And safe remedies for diseases and animal pests are listed in easy-to-use charts.

You'll use this manual in all seasons, during planting, maintenance, and harvest. Because it's so easy to scan for answers, you won't waste precious hours sifting through unnecessary prose.

HOW to grow 62 of the most popular vegetables, fruits, nuts & herbs.

WHEN to harvest and how to store the fruits of your labor.

HOW much to plant to feed your family.

WHAT are the dozens of ally & companion plants. *A separate Chart shows how they work and where they've been tested.*

WHERE to order all the varieties. *A separate list gives supplier information.*

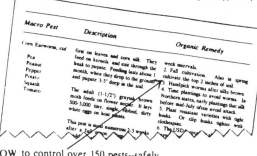

HOW to control over 150 pests--safely.

WHICH disease-resistant, regional and specialty varieties to choose.

Organic Garden Vegetables

This book is packed with exact information that gives all gardeners quick answers to difficult problems. Whether you are a beginner or an expert, the easy-to-use format puts precise details at your fingertips in seconds.

Easy-to-reference facts on climate, soil preparation, planting, crop care, harvesting, kitchen ideas and exact details on growing over 300 varieties of vegetables.

A complete practical guide to over 500 diseases, insects and problems that affect vegetables. The easy-to-read style makes this book a quick, easy reference you'll be turning to for years.

Available April, 1991 - 144 pages 8 1/2" X 11" **$9.95**

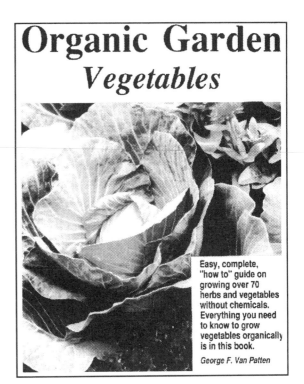

Organic Garden
Vegetables

Easy, complete, "how to" guide on growing over 70 herbs and vegetables without chemicals. Everything you need to know to grow vegetables organically is in this book.

George F. Van Patten

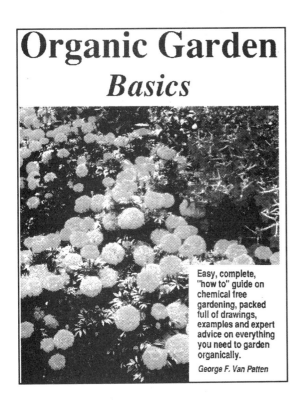

Organic Garden
Basics

Easy, complete, "how to" guide on chemical free gardening, packed full of drawings, examples and expert advice on everything you need to garden organically.

George F. Van Patten

Available August 1992 - 160 pages 8 1/2" X 11" **$12.95**

Organic Garden Basics

Every year home gardeners dump ten times more chemicals on their gardens than commercial farmers. These toxic substances contaminate ground water and pollute the environment, threatening our existence. With just a little care and management this problem can be avoided.

This comprehensive, practical manual is packed full of basic "how to" examples that make organic gardening fun, simple, safe and easy. Beginners and experts alike will find countless handy, time saving answers and ideas in this easy-to-use guide.

How to build soil, compost, fertilize, conserve water, stop weeds, buy seeds and plants, grow flowers, vegetables, shrubs and trees, natural pest control, container gardens, garden gear and much more are included in this complete handbook.

About the author:

George F. Van Patten puts more than twenty years of gardening experience at your fingertips with this series of organic garden books. His expert advise has helped thousands of gardeners turn simple, yet effective organic gardening techniques into bountiful landscapes. He has owned and operated landscape businesses and a retail garden center which gives him the hands on experience necessary to explain exactly what you need to know to grow the best garden possible. He resides in Oregon where he continues to write and maintain a delightful suburban organic garden.

Gardening : The Rockwool Book

112 pages, 8 1/2 x 11", illustrated, index, **$14.95**

This book is packed with the newest information on the revolutionary new hydroponic growing medium, rockwool. The easy step-by-step instructions show you how to grow the best possible garden in rockwool.

Rockwool is the biggest innovation in growing mediums since sterilized soil. This revolutionary new soilless medium consists of thin strand-like fibers made from rocks.

Growing hydroponically without soil is very productive and easy Rockwool gardens yield 10 to 20 percent more than soil gardens. This easy-to-achieve yield coupled with a few simple cultivation techniques can make rockwool produce twice as much as soil.

Cut irrigation by more than half when using rockwool This new medium holds 10-14 times more water than soil, which makes it ideal to grow deck and patio plants in containers.

Gardening Indoors

144 pages, 8 1/2 x 11", illustrated, index, **$14.95**

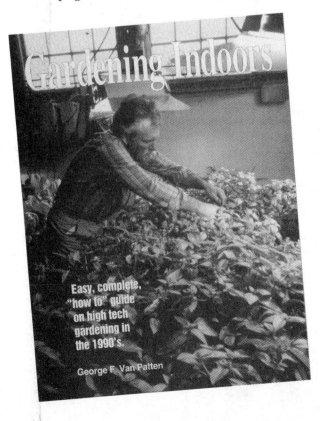

Order Form

Gardening Indoors	$14.95
Gardening: The Rockwool Book	14.95
Organic Garden Vegetables	9.95
Organic Garden Basics	12.95
Gardening at a Glance	22.95
Backyard Composting	6.95

Shipping, handling & insurance $3.00 for 1 book

Call for shipping costs of more than 1 book.

Ship to:

Name _____

Address _____

City _____ State ___ Zip _____

Telephone (_____) _____

_____ Check _____ Money Order _____ Credit Card

Order Toll Free 1-800-345-0096

Publisher's Distribution Service
121 East Front Street, Suite 203
Traverse City, MI 49684